TRACKING DOWN PARTICLES

R. D. Hill
University of Illinois

W. A. BENJAMIN, INC.

New York   *Amsterdam*   ▼ 1964

TRACKING DOWN PARTICLES

Library of Congress Catalog Card Number 63–11723
Manufactured in the United States of America

Final manuscript was put into production on November 28, 1962; this volume was published on June 15, 1963; second printing, with corrections, April 30, 1964

The publisher wishes to acknowledge the assistance of Paul Orban, who produced the illustrations, and William Prokos, who designed the dust jacket

W. A. BENJAMIN, INC.
2465 Broadway, New York 25, New York

EDITOR'S FOREWORD

There are two ways to introduce an elementary book whose professed purpose is explaining the mysteries of modern physics to persons who have had little or no formal training in physics. One way is to start by reviewing fundamental, well-established physical principles and concepts, after which the reader can understand how unexpectedly and profoundly different from classical (pre-1900) physics is the modern view of nature. This way is logical, but is likely to defeat the book's purpose, because the reader has to fight his way through many, many pages of necessary but not very exciting information before he reaches the material on modern physics. The second way is less usual and less logical, namely, to plunge right into modern physics, without worrying too much about whether the reader is clearly grasping all the novel ideas being so rapidly presented to him. This is the way this book has been written, in the hope that the reader's interest can be immediately captured and held to the end of the book, even though he finds much of the material puzzling. Once he has seen what modern physics is about, it should be easier (so we trust) to hold his attention through a review of the classical foundations of present-day physics.

The reader is urged, therefore, to give the book a thorough but relatively rapid first reading, straight through without looking ahead to the review of classical physics or to the Glossary. Then, after reading the review and the Glossary, we hope he will want to read the first four chapters again, and that he will enjoy doing so, because he will find many points that escaped him the first time. In this way we hope that the book will bring our readers to an appreciation of the fascinating, wonderful, puzzling, scarcely believable world of modern physics research.

EDWARD GERJUOY

Princeton, New Jersey
March 1963

PREFACE

This book gives an account of man's quest for fundamental particles—those pieces of matter and energy, so small as to appear physically indivisible, that make up our material world. To date (1963) physicists have discovered 32 different forms of particles that might be considered fundamental; but the list is not now, and may never be, complete. As experimental techniques improve, more particles may be discovered, many of which may be considered simply as associations of other particles. Or it may be that our very methods of exploring whether particles are elementary or composite necessarily introduce a bias into our answer; we may never be able to decide what is fundamental.

This book was written for the interested non-scientist as well as the introductory student of science. I have therefore avoided complicated theoretical and mathematical arguments in my attempt to show how, and by whom, the various particles were discovered and their properties understood. Difficult concepts have been introduced only where the clarity of the exposition would have suffered without them; and, wherever possible, I have used pictorial methods to illustrate basic principles.

That high-energy (particle) physics is considered immensely important today is affirmed by the public support it receives; the world's major governments invest large efforts in the construction of high-energy accelerators and associated research projects. Although the physicist is usually well aware of, and often concerned about, the political and economic implications of his research, he tracks down particles, not for political or economic reasons, but because the hunt itself is fascinating and rewarding from a purely scientific point of view. Each new particle discovered provides him with another intriguing piece to be fitted into the jigsaw puzzle of our physical world.

It is a pleasure to thank the many people who have assisted me in putting this account together. They include Dr. Edward Gerjuoy, editor of this Benjamin series and author of one portion of this volume; Dr. Maurice Goldhaber, Director of Brookhaven National Laboratory; Professors Edwin Goldwasser, David Jackson, David Pines, and Mrs. Margaret Runkel, my colleagues at the University of Illinois. Finally, I should like to give particular thanks to my wife, Judith, and to my son, Robert B. Hill.

R. D. HILL

Urbana, Illinois
March 1963

ACKNOWLEDGMENTS

The author wishes to acknowledge the following publishers and authors who gave permission and generously supplied material for the figures listed:

J. J. Thomson's positive ray apparatus, p. 2 (*The Director, Science Museum, London, England*)

Laura and Enrico Fermi, p. 18 (*Mrs. L. Fermi, Chicago, Illinois*)

Niels Bohr and H. Yukawa, p. 26 (*General Dynamics Corporation, San Diego, California*)

Meson jet, p. 29, from *The Study of Elementary Particles by the Photographic Method,* Pergamon, New York, 1958, Plate 15–11, p. 553 (*Prof. C. F. Powell, Bristol University, Bristol, England*)

Pi-Mu-e decays, p. 34 (*Prof. R. Hildebrand, University of Chicago, Illinois*)

Associated production of Λ^0 and K^0, p. 46 (*Brookhaven National Laboratory, Upton, Long Island, New York*)

Production of Xi and anti-Xi Particles, p. 50 (*Brookhaven National Laboratory*)

CONTENTS

one

ELECTRONS, ATOMS, AND NUCLEI

"He is very pleasant in conversation and is not fossilized at all . . . shaves, very badly, wears his hair rather long. . . ." So wrote young Ernest Rutherford about his professor, J. J. Thomson, of the University of Cambridge, England, in 1895. Only two years later, Thomson was to discover the electron and lay the basis for present-day electronic physics. Twenty-five years later, Rutherford was to occupy Thomson's position as head of the same laboratory and was to create the subject of nuclear physics.

It is just over 60 years since the electron saw birth as a particle known to man. Its name had already been coined 10 years earlier by Johnstone Stoney, who established its charge. Stoney used the word *electron* to denote an elementary charge only, and he had no idea of the electron as a particle. At a conference on the "free" electron, held in 1956 to commemorate the 100th anniversary of the birth of J. J. Thomson, his

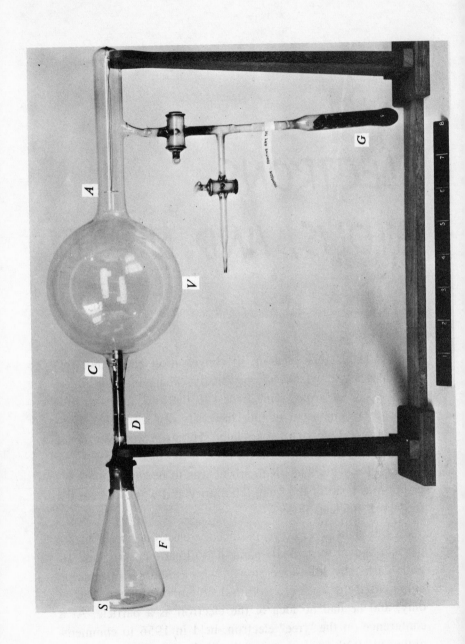

Thomson Positive-Ray Tube

The original Thomson electron tube does not appear to have survived, but Thomson's positive ray tube, which is very similar, is now exhibited in London's Science Museum. A photograph of this tube is shown by permission of the Director of the Science Museum.

The pressure of gas in vessels V and F could be reduced and controlled by immersing tube G, containing absorbent charcoal, in liquid air. A discharge in the gas was created in the vessel V by connecting a high voltage between A and C. With a positive voltage on A, the positive rays or ions were caused to move toward C, at which electrode many ions managed to pass through the hole in C and then along the tube D into the vessel F. While the ions were passing along D, Thomson observed that the ions could be deflected to one side by magnetic and electric fields, and he was able to measure the ion displacements on the scintillation screen S on the end of vessel F.

son G. P. Thomson said: "My father's measurement of the charge-to-mass ratio of the particle, the electron, appeared in a lecture at the Royal Institution of London on 30th April 1897, and was published a fortnight later in the *Electrician* . . . The proof was completed in 1899 by the simultaneous measurement of the charge-to-mass ratio and the charge of electrons . . . This showed that he had found something very much smaller, at least a thousand times smaller, than the hydrogen atom, and something, and this was much more important, something which was a universal constituent of all matter." One might add, to continue Rutherford's observations on J. J. Thomson, that little did the long-haired physicist of the nineteenth century realize he had founded something very large, namely, an era of electronics, an era of the radio and the television tube.

A motionless electron is the lightest material particle known. It is so light that it would require 30 thousand million million million million (3×10^{28}) of them to weigh 1 ounce. It is a constituent of every material object on the earth. It is the negatively charged part of matter as we know it. Matter is made up of neutral atoms, that is, atoms which have as much negatively charged electricity in them as positively charged electricity. Electrons are the negative electricity of atoms. In dreaming up a scientific apparatus to measure the electrical charge and the mass of an electron, J. J. Thomson invented an electron tube, which was the forerunner of the television tube of today.

Structure of the atom

The discovery of the positively electrified part of the atom also dates from about the turn of the nineteenth century. Positive rays in gaseous-discharge tubes, which today are seen everywhere in neon lights, were first studied by the German physicist, Goldstein, in 1886. In 1910, J. J. Thomson again was the first to show, by the same technique he used in his earlier electron tube, that positive rays were individual atoms from which electrons had been stripped. The element hydrogen possesses the simplest atom. Hydrogen-gas particles actually consist of two atoms joined together to form a molecule. This has been known since the nineteenth century, the time of the atom chemist, Dalton. The chemists of that period did not know that the hydrogen atom is itself composite, consisting of a central positive part, known as a proton, and an outer part of equal negative charge, which is an electron. A proton and an electron in a hydrogen atom are held together by the electric attraction of their opposite charges, much as the earth is kept in the solar system by the gravitational force exerted by the sun. The simplest "modern" picture of the hydrogen atom is the so-called Rutherford-Bohr atom, which is a not-altogether-consistent blend of *classical* (pre-1900) and *quantum* physics. In the 1913 Bohr picture of the hydrogen atom, the electron finally settles down in an innermost circular *Bohr orbit,* at a distance of about 5 thousandths of a millionth of a centimeter (5×10^{-9} cm) from the proton. A more modern and consistent theory pertaining to atomic structure, dating from about 1930, is harder to picture than the Bohr theory.

Thomson was not highly accurate in his first measurement of the electron mass: The proton, which makes up most of the hydrogen atom's mass, is now known to be 1836 times heavier than the electron. Approximately 17 million million million million (1.7×10^{25}) protons, and the same number of electrons, in hydrogen atoms are required to make up 1 ounce of hydrogen gas. One of the most puzzling and unanswered questions of today is why matter should be so concentrated in the proton and why this proton should be so stable compared with other neighboring particles of similar mass. Fortunately for the stability of the material universe, protons are now known to possess an average life of at least 100 million million million million (10^{26}) years.

The Hydrogen Atom

Diagram (a) gives a rough picture of the quantum-mechanical description of a hydrogen atom in its most common *stable* state. The hydrogen nucleus—a proton—lies at the center of a spherical-shaped electron cloud. The density of the electron cloud is such that a sphere at a radius of approximately 5×10^{-9} centimeter from the nucleus would intercept more of the cloud than at any other radius. This happens to be just the radius where, according to the Bohr theory of the atom, the electron was permitted to circulate.

In the Bohr theory, the electron could be precisely located in its orbit at any instant, just as the Earth can be precisely located in its orbit at any time of the year. According to present quantum-mechanical ideas, it is impossible to definitely localize an electron at any time, although in the hydrogen atom it is highly probable that the electron will be in the vicinity of 5×10^{-9} centimeter from the proton. Diagram (b) shows the manner in which the electron clouds—one from each atom—are distorted when two hydrogen atoms join to form a hydrogen molecule. In the stable form of the hydrogen molecule, the two protons are separated by approximately 7.5×10^{-9} centimeter. The proton sizes (10^{-13} centimeter) are too insignificant to be seen here.

Atomic elements of matter

The natural building-up of atoms was, and still is, a challenging problem for study. The stories of the ancient alchemists and their search for the philosopher's stone, which would change one element into another, are well known. Needless to say, no such stone was ever found and, today, we know it is idle to look for any transmutation apart from a source of nuclear particles. We have seen that the proton is the basic center or nucleus of the hydrogen atom. According to the Rutherford-Bohr model of the atom, all elements consist of positively charged and massive nuclei surrounded by just the right number of electrons to neutralize the positive central charge. Different elements are distinguished by having different numbers of positive nuclear charges (called atomic numbers) and correspondingly different numbers of electrons in their outer atomic regions. In nature, as we know it on our earth and within our planetary and galactic systems, there are on the order of 100 elements with different positive nuclear charges.

The history of the discovery of elements is, in itself, an interesting aspect of nuclear physics. Naturally occurring elements have atomic numbers from 1 through 92. Until 1932, all known elements up to those with an atomic number of 83 had a stable form, whereas elements from 84 through 92 were known only in radioactive forms. By the year 1932, all but four places had been filled in the entire element list through 92. In 1937 the gap at number 43 was filled by an element which was "manufactured" in the nuclear-physics laboratory. This element, which is now known as technetium, has at least 12 forms, all of which are radioactive. It is interesting to note that, even though this element does not naturally occur on the earth, its presence has been demonstrated in stars, where undoubtedly it is currently being manufactured in much the same manner as the physicist produces it in his laboratory. In 1941, the second gap, at atomic number 61, was filled by an artificially produced element known as promethium. This element is also known to exist only in radioactive forms. The two remaining gaps, at atomic numbers 85 and 87, were similarly filled by artificially produced elements. They were also shown to occur naturally in exceedingly small amounts. These last two elements, like the others between 84 and 92, occur only in radioactive forms.

In 1940, the first artificially produced element with an atomic number greater than 92 was clearly identified. Since this time, many new elements of higher and higher atomic numbers have been added, so that, at the beginning of the 1960s, we were familiar with no less than 103 different elements. The last of the naturally occurring elements is uranium, at position 92. The first of the transuranic elements, as they are called, is neptunium with atomic number 93. The logic of how this element acquired its name is very obvious and in some ways unsatisfactory, for with the next element, number 94, named plutonium, the namers ran out of planets. However, as all the other transuranic elements up to the present time have been discovered at the Lawrence Radiation Laboratory of the University of California, Berkeley, it is not unaccountable that many of the names applied to the new elements have Western associations. Thus, element 95 is named americium, element 97 is called berkelium, element 98 is californium, and the last-found element, number 103, lawrencium, is named after the founder of the laboratory. The remainder of the transuranic elements are named after famous scientists: 96, curium; 99, einsteinium; 100, fermium and 101, mendelevium. One element, number 102, has not yet received a generally accepted name. Its discovery was first announced in 1957 by a group of physicists working at the Nobel Institute, in Sweden. Its discovery, however, was disputed by the well-established group in Berkeley, who claimed that no such element could have been manufactured in the Swedish experiments. The Berkeley group has subsequently identified atoms of element 102. Such claims and counter-claims in the field of discovery of new elements have always been with us. We note, however, only two recent cases: element 61, formerly known as illinium, after the state of Illinois in which the element was reputedly found, and element 43, which used to be known as masurium after Masuria, a region of East Prussia that the apparent discoverer wished to honor.

Basic particles in atomic nuclei

Now, although the charges of the naturally occurring elemental nuclei vary between 1 and 92 in units of the proton's charge, the masses of these nuclei vary from 1 to 238 in units of the proton's mass: 1 is the mass of the simplest hydrogen atom; 238 is the mass of one of the uranium atoms. It follows that there must be another constituent of nuclei that, although adding to the mass, does not contribute to the nuclear charge. In the uranium atom of mass 238 there are only 92 protons, but there must be 146 equivalent proton masses from another neutral constituent. This neutral additive to nuclei was sought by many different physicists for over 20 years. It was discovered by Chadwick, of Cambridge University, England, only in 1932. At that time Chadwick was Rutherford's right-hand man, and it is clear from Rutherford's earlier papers that many attempts at Cambridge had already been made to find such a neutral particle. Chadwick did not just stumble on the discovery of the neutron (as the neutral particle was named). Through being alerted to the expected properties of a neutron, Chadwick saw in the puzzling experiments of the German physicist Bothe and in the "almost-had-it" experiments of the French physicists Curie-Joliots the tell-tale signs of the neutral particle he sought. From the discovery of the neutron in 1932 can be traced the upsurge of present-day nuclear physics. The neutron, with approximately the same mass as the proton, but with no net charge, immediately became the key to solving nuclear structure. In nuclear fission as well, the neutron proved to be the firing pin that unleashes the tremendous energies lying in nuclear matter.

"It is obvious," said Chadwick in his original paper, "that this neutron may help us to visualize the building up of complex (nuclear) structures." Chadwick went on pessimistically: "But the discussion of these matters will not be pursued further, for such speculations, though not idle, are not at the moment fruitful. It is of course, possible to suppose that the neutron may be an elementary particle. This view has little to recommend it at the present, except the possibility of explaining the statistics of nuclei. . . ." It has turned out that the neutron is, in fact, an elementary particle and that all the nuclei can be regarded as built up out of the building blocks of neutrons and protons. Of course, in the laboratory we are not able at present to make any particular nucleus by merely adding together neutrons and protons directly in this way. However, this is almost certainly the manner in which elements are synthesized in stars, an example of which occurs even in our own sun.

The way in which neutrons and protons are held together is a basic problem of nuclear physics that still holds our attention. It is quite clear that intense forces of attraction, which do not extend out very far from the particles, exist between neutrons and protons. In order to break the particles apart, high-energy sources, either of nuclear projectiles or γ (gamma) rays, are required.

Matter and antimatter

Before leaving the subject of atoms and nuclei, we shall discuss a question that may have occurred to the reader because of our earlier references to matter "as we know it on our earth." We can see no reason why nuclear matter should be only positively charged and why only negative electrons should surround these nuclei so as to make atoms. Physicists know, however, that this is the only kind of matter that surrounds us on our earth and in our own planetary and galactic systems. Evidence from cosmic rays indicates that planetary and galactic protons and neutrons are the same as on our earth. However, other kinds of neutrons and protons can be made in the high-energy-physics laboratory. These are the so-called antimatter particles. In principle, there is really no reason why matter, rather than antimatter, should exist. Negatively charged nuclei could be surrounded by positively charged electrons to form antiatoms. However, it is also known that antiparticles cannot exist simultaneously with ordinary-matter particles. It happens in nature that opposite kinds of particles destroy one another; that is, they annihilate each other. The details of the discovery of antiparticles must now be very briefly told.

This account starts in 1931. The English theoretical physicist, Dirac, interpreted a mathematical wave equation, now known as the Dirac equation, as indicating the formal existence of an antiparticle. For an electron in particular, the antiparticle would have the same mass as the electron but a positive instead of a negative charge. Dirac must have pondered over this unexpected conclusion with some misgivings because, in order to extricate his theory from the lack of experimental evidence supporting the existence of such a particle, he first suggested that a proton should probably be identified with the positively charged electron. Nature, however, was not to be misled and within the same year Anderson, a cosmic-ray physicist working in Pasadena, California, found cloud-chamber tracks of electron-mass particles that bent in the opposite direction in a magnetic field from that accepted for negatively charged particles. These positively charged electrons are sometimes called positrons, and they are, in fact, the antimatter counterparts of ordinary electrons. Dirac also predicted in detail what would happen to positrons—they would be attracted to negative electrons and, upon meeting together, would disappear; two x rays would then be emitted in opposite directions with the velocity of light. That is, matter would annihilate antimatter, and the mass energy of the 2 particles would convert into radiation. It was experimentally observed that positrons annihilate in precisely this manner. For the experimental discovery of the positron, Anderson was awarded the Nobel Prize of 1936, sharing it that year with Hess, the discoverer of cosmic rays. Dirac was awarded a Nobel Prize

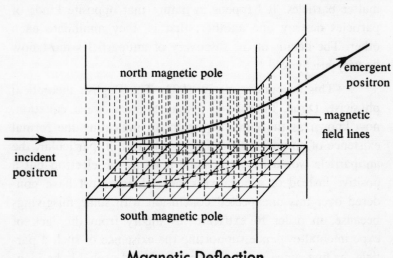

Magnetic Deflection

When an energetic electron enters a magnetic field it is deflected from its straight-line path. If the field is constant and if the electron is moving perpendicularly across the field, the deflected path will be an arc of a circle. This is shown in the diagram where the projection of the path of a positively charged electron is indicated on the pole of the magnet. The invisible magnetic field, which is, of course, everywhere between the north and south poles, is indicated by the screen of dotted lines.

in 1933, sharing it on this occasion with Schrödinger for the formal development of quantum mechanics. From this period can be traced the intense effort by physicists to discover the antiproton.

The antiproton was not discovered for another quarter of a century. In these intervening years certain outstanding physicists began to doubt the general existence of antimatter. Some argued that antiprotons and antineutrons couldn't exist because, if they did, our ordinary matter particles would have a funnel down which they could continuously disappear into energy. Although physicists are not a strongly wagering fraternity, a number of bets were actually laid for and against

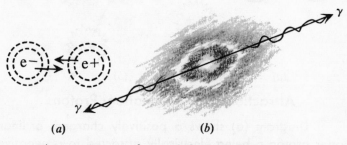

(a)   *(b)*

Attraction and Annihilation; Electrons

Diagram (a) shows a negative, ordinary-matter electron being attracted by, and also attracting, a positive antimatter electron. In (b) is shown their disappearance a moment later when they have annihilated one another.

The two γ symbols represent radiation energy that is sent out in opposite directions with the velocity of light. No energy is lost in the annihilation process: The γ rays have the same energies as the mass-equivalent energies of the electrons, that is, approximately ½ million electron volts each. These γ rays are of the same nature as x rays, which in this case would be produced from an x-ray tube working at a voltage of ½ million volts.

the appearance of the antiprotons. Strenuous efforts were made in the 1950s by experimental cosmic-ray physicists to get on the track of antimatter. In the meantime, the machine builders were mercilessly closing the energy gap between the available accelerated-particle energy and that required, according to

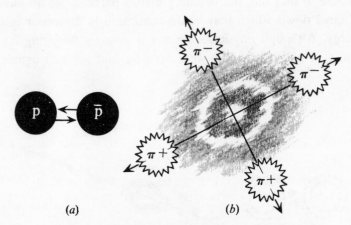

(a)   (b)

Attraction and Annihilation; Protons

Diagram (a) shows a positively charged, ordinary-matter proton p being electrically attracted to a negatively charged, antimatter proton p̄ (commonly called p bar).

Sketch (b) shows the annihilation of p and p̄ and the production of four π mesons. These are set free with high velocities. The average number of π mesons produced by annihilation of a low-energy proton and antiproton is between four and five, but there is a wide variation. In any case, the total energy of the π mesons, including their equivalent mass-energy, is exactly equal to the total energy of the proton and antiproton before annihilation.

This process might not appear to represent a destruction of nuclear matter, but the fact is that the π mesons themselves will eventually break up, so that all that will remain are γ rays and neutrinos.

Dirac's theory, to produce an antiproton. With an eye on this problem, physicists at the University of California at Berkeley, deliberately designed a machine to produce 6.3-billion-electron-volt protons. The minimum laboratory energy necessary to produce an antiproton in a collision between two ordinary protons is, according to Dirac's theory, approximately 6.0 Bev (billion electron volts). In 1953, the machine was working but was not yet well-enough tamed for an attempt on this problem. Particle counters were also required in which one antiproton could be detected in the presence of millions of other confusing secondary particles. By the following year, however, the intensity of the machine beam was high enough, and particle-detector apparatus had been developed highly enough to institute a definite search program. In the summer of 1954, antiprotons were observed for the first time. They had been produced very weakly, to the extent of only a few antiprotons for approximately every hundred thousand million collisions of the high-energy positively charged protons accelerated in the machine. This work was recognized by the award of the Nobel Prize in 1958 to Segrè and Chamberlain of Berkeley, California.

This discovery, however, still leaves unanswered the great question of where, if at all, antimatter naturally exists. Goldhaber has suggested that there are, in fact, two universes: our own and our antimatter counterpart, which are now very distant from one another and are still separating at a prodigious speed close to the velocity of light. But the search is nevertheless on again! Cosmic-ray experimenters and space physicists are busily trying to pinpoint any tell-tale annihilation radiation from antimatter-ordinary matter combinations taking place in space.

two

LEPTONS, MESONS, AND STRANGE PARTICLES

By the early 1930s, physicists were occupied with two very puzzling questions, both of which were connected with the nuclear particles, the neutron and proton. The first question concerned the subject of beta decay of a nucleus. Niels Bohr, one of the most highly revered physicists of the twentieth century and the one who gave us a quantum theory of the atom, said in the Faraday Lecture in 1932: "At the present stage of atomic theory we may say that we have no argument, either empirical or theoretical, for upholding the energy principle in the case of beta-ray disintegrations." In an historic understatement he added, ". . . in the atomic theory, notwithstanding all the recent progress, we must still be prepared for surprises." A beta particle is another scientific term for an electron that is emitted from a radioactive nucleus, that is, a nucleus that is in an unstable condition of equilibrium and that will decay spontaneously into a more stable variety of nucleus. The puzzling question of beta decay was that the energy taken off by the beta particle was rarely found to equal the difference of the total energies of the radioactive nucleus before decay and the resulting nucleus after decay. Such an unbalanced phenomenon, which apparently refuted the conservation-of-energy principle, as Bohr said, had hitherto never been observed in nature.

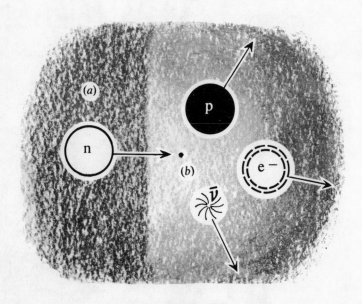

Neutron Decay

A neutron n at (a) is shown decaying at (b). The products of the beta decay are: an electron e⁻, an antineutrino ν̄, and a residual proton p. The antineutrino is made as inconspicuous as possible, in fact its path would not be discernible by any normal means.

The neutrino hypothesis

Although many hundreds of different cases of beta decay are known today, the most elementary beta decay that exists is the disintegration of a neutron into a proton and an electron. A neutron always decays if it is free. On the average, a free neutron can *live* only approximately 1000 seconds. A neutron that decays in a radioactive nucleus may live either considerably longer or considerably shorter than 1000 seconds depending upon the nature of the nucleus. For simplicity, then, let us consider the problem of beta decay of a free neutron; we then state immediately how the puzzle was solved. When a neutron decays into a proton by emitting an electron, the problem of the missing energy is solved if, at the same time as the electron is emitted, another invisible particle is involved. Surely this seems like either an obvious answer or a dangerous proposal. We shall see that it was indeed far from obvious and, in fact, could only have been suggested by a person with a very deep insight. On this occasion the person was Pauli, Nobel Laureate in 1945 for an entirely different contribution to modern physics, namely, the discovery of the exclusion principle, also called the *Pauli principle*. In 1931, Pauli hypothesized the existence of an entirely new particle, which the Italian physicist, Fermi, was soon afterward to call a *neutrino*. This particle is the "little" neutral one, as distinct from the "big" neutral one, the neutron. In order that the neutrino should be "invisible," it has to be electrically neutral; also, in order that (at least on some very rare occasions) a beta particle should take all the energy that is available between the initial and final nuclei, the neutrino is required to have a vanishingly

Laura and Enrico Fermi

A photograph taken at the University of Chicago shortly before Enrico Fermi's death in 1954.

small mass by virtue of the principle of mass-energy conservation. Whereas charge and mass are quantities a neutrino cannot possess, there is one property that it decidedly must have, and this is undoubtedly what made Pauli so sure of his suggestion. The neutrino must possess spin. The neutron, proton, and electron all have spin; indeed, each particle has the same amount of spin, which we shall term 1 quantum of spin. Since the beta decay of a neutron starts with just 1 particle having only 1 quantum of spin, it can be shown from the rules for combining spins that, with only 2 output particles (for example, a proton and an electron), there is no way of adding 2 quanta of spin together so as to get the same amount of spin as at the start. It has been found experimentally that spin, like energy and momentum, is always conserved in a nuclear reaction. With 3 outgoing particles—proton, electron, and neutrino—it is possible, by pointing their separate spins in the right directions, to obtain the same combined spin as the neutron had at the start (diagram, page 22).

Although spin is one very definite characteristic of a neutrino, the spin of an invisible, massless particle is still a very difficult thing to think about trying to measure. The rather fantastic part of the neutrino story is that, although the neutrino is virtually undetectable, it has irrefutably been proved to exist. Two very beautiful, and very difficult, experiments have been performed: one to measure the recoil, or momentum, imparted by a neutrino to both the beta particle and the residual nucleus when a neutrino departs from them with high energy; the other to demonstrate that when an energetic neutrino is absorbed by a proton (an event occurring very infrequently) it causes a neutron and positron to be produced. The latter experiment is known as inverse beta decay of the neutron. The former experiment was performed in the 1950s, mainly by Allen and his collaborators at the University of Illinois; the latter experiment was carried out by Cowan and Reines at the Los Alamos Laboratory, also in the 1950s. Many years before these experiments were performed, however, Bohr remarked: ". . . the grounds for serious doubts as regards the strict validity of the conservation laws in the problem of the emission of beta rays . . . are now largely removed by the agreement between the rapidly increasing experimental evidence . . . and the consequences of Pauli's neutrino hypothesis, so remarkably developed in Fermi's theory."

Origin of binding forces in nucleus

The second puzzling problem was to understand the nature of the strong attractive forces that must exist not only between neutrons and protons but between neutrons and neutrons and protons and protons. It became clear by the 1930s, from studies of existing nuclei and their interactions with high-speed nuclear projectiles, that nuclear forces must be approximately the same, no matter which pairs of the basic nuclear particles were involved, and that these forces must be of very short range. In addition, they must also be very much stronger than the electric forces that exist between all charged bodies.

In certain respects we shall consider neutrons and protons that are inside nuclei on an equal basis and call them by a generic term *nucleons*. A most interesting and important observation was made on nuclei when the sizes of many of them were systematically studied. It was found that the nucleon density, that is, the number of nucleons in a nucleus divided by its nuclear volume, is practically the same for all nuclei. This result implies that each nucleon in any nucleus is influenced by only a few of its nearest neighbors. This property is usually described by saying that nuclear forces are *saturated*. If, on the contrary, a nucleon were strongly influenced by every one of its associates in a nucleus, that is, if nuclear forces were unsaturated, it would no doubt have been observed that the large nuclei have significantly higher densities than the small nuclei. At the time this conclusion was reached concern-

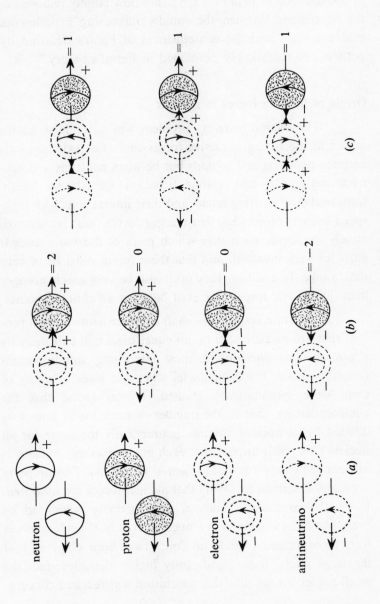

Spin Orientations

The quantum rules for a particle with a single quantum of spin assert that, having picked a direction for the spin axis, the spin can have only two orientations, namely, either parallel or antiparallel to that axis.

In (a) are shown the two possible spin orientations for each of the four particles—neutron, proton, electron, and antineutrino. In (b) it is seen that none of the four possible combinations of electron and proton spin can add up to one quantum of spin, the original spin of the neutron. Combining the electron and proton spins gives either 0, 2, or —2 quanta of spin along the original spin direction.

In (c) it is seen that there are a number of ways whereby three spins of the antineutrino, electron, and proton, each of one quantum, can be combined to give one quantum of spin.

These diagrammatic representations of quantum-mechanical spin vectors are not conclusive, of course, but it can be shown using rigorous mathematics that the conclusions drawn from the above diagrams are correct. Moreover, surprising as it may seem on classical grounds, it can be shown that conclusions insisting that the spin must be oriented either parallel or antiparallel to any one axis are not inconsistent with the assertion that this axis could have been oriented in any arbitrary direction. This is an example of the way quantum mechanics demands revision of classical preconceptions.

ing nuclei, the property of saturation was not wholly a new idea. Other instances of saturation were already known, such as in the binding together of atoms. Although the binding of 2 hydrogen atoms to form a molecule of hydrogen is a fundamentally different problem from the one of nuclear binding, there are still some interesting analogies that deserve discussion. For instance, a molecule of hydrogen is saturated in the sense that it does not tend to bind another hydrogen atom to it. Similarly, an alpha particle, which contains 2 protons and 2 neutrons, will not bind another nucleon—a nucleus of mass 5 does not exist. The forces in the two cases are, of course, entirely different. The force between two hydrogen atoms has an electric origin. From a pictorial viewpoint, the molecular-hydrogen binding arises because the 2 electrons, one from each hydrogen atom, exchange backward and forward from one atom to the other. (It is true that the electrons cannot exchange in an arbitrary way. Unless the spins of the 2 electrons are in opposite directions to one another, the 2 atoms will not bind.) The saturation of the hydrogen-molecule-binding forces comes about because it is possible to exchange only 2 electrons, which have the same energies, in hydrogen atoms. (Consistent with the Pauli principle, a third hydrogen atom is not allowed to have an electron of the same energy as the electrons in the other two atoms.) The saturation of nuclear forces arises in a more complicated way—there are a number of contributing factors, including the shortness of the range of interaction of nuclear forces, which bring about the effect of saturation. (Nevertheless, there is also an exchange type of force that, in the presence of the Pauli principle applied to nucleons, also gives rise to a saturation. It is mainly this factor that prevents the binding of a fifth nucleon to an alpha particle.) With this brief discussion of saturation of forces, we can perhaps understand why Heisenberg originally suggested, in 1933, that the attraction between a neutron and a proton might also be ascribed to the exchange of a charged particle from one nucleon to another.

Fermi and others, in 1934, investigated the consequences of a theory in which the electron was exchanged but found the force too weak. In 1935, the Japanese physicist, Yukawa, put forward the bold idea that the nuclear force was

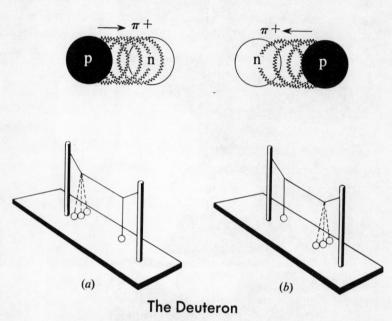

(a)   (b)

The Deuteron

The simplest association of a proton p and a neutron n is in a deuteron, which, because it has a charge equal to the proton, is a chemical isotope of hydrogen. The nuclear force arises from the forward and backward exchange of a "virtual," not an actual, π meson between the neutron and proton. Probably the simplest mechanical analogy of this exchange is a system of two identical pendulums hanging from the same loosely stretched wire. If one pendulum is set swinging, it will soon communicate its oscillations across the stretched wire so that the other pendulum will eventually take all the oscillation, and the original one will come to a stop. The reverse process will then commence. A certain amount of energy can be regarded as residing in the transfer oscillation. It is this energy of coupling that corresponds to the π meson.

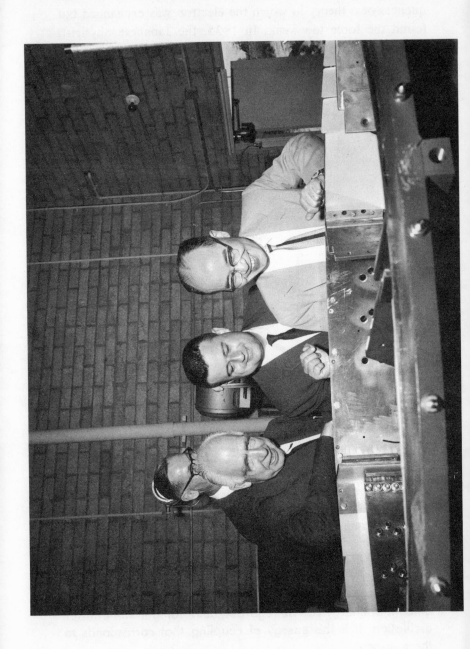

due to the exchange of an entirely new type of particle for which, from the range of the nuclear force, he could predict a mass a few hundred times that of an electron. These ideas were published in the then-little-known journal, *The Proceedings of the Physico-Mathematical Society of Japan,* where they might well have remained in temporary oblivion but for the erudition of J. R. Oppenheimer. He drew attention to Yukawa's brilliant suggestion, and this supplied the impetus to the experimental search for the new particle. Just before World War II, in a period when minds were occupied with the darkening political situation in Europe, experimental indications, rather meager at first, were obtained of an intermediate-mass particle (a meson, as it is now called) heavier than an electron but lighter than a proton. These observations were made by Anderson and collaborators at the California Institute of Technology, and by Street and Stevenson at Harvard University.

Mesons—other fundamental particles

It is not quite true to suggest that no pure, nuclear-physics research was performed during the war years of 1939 to 1945. There was, of course, a tremendous amount of

Bohr and Yukawa

Niels Bohr (*left*) and Hideki Yukawa (*right*) shown inspecting experiments at the John Jay Hopkins Laboratory in 1959. The physicists associated with the laboratory are Marshall Rosenbluth (*center*) and Donald Kerst (*in background*). Kerst was the inventor of the betatron in 1940 (see Chapter Three).

nuclear-physical data amassed in connection with nuclear fission during these years, but the pace of really basic, high-energy nuclear-physics research did slow down. There was, however, one experiment in this field that one might say was carried out despite the war. In a basement in Rome, hidden away from both the Nazis and Fascists alike, three young Italian physicists, Conversi, Pancini, and Piccioni, measured the rate at which positive mesons decayed and negative mesons were absorbed in materials. They were observing mesons produced by cosmic rays somewhere near the top of the earth's atmosphere. However, because of their very high energies, the mesons penetrated through the air to counters in the basement laboratory. Their experiment indicated that these mesons had quite long lives of a few millionths of a second. All was not well, however, for the mesons of Yukawa's nuclear forces should have been taken up by the nuclear matter in much less time. Fermi and Teller estimated this at 100 million millionth (10^{-14}) of a second.

Another very significant step in experimental techniques had also been made just as World War II began. Powell, at the University of Bristol, in collaboration with Waller of Ilford Laboratories (London), succeeded in producing a photographic emulsion highly sensitive to ionizing nuclear particles. Immediately after the war, this technique was applied to an investigation of cosmic-ray particles, and a spectacular break-through by Powell, Occhialini, and Lattes was made in 1947. Emulsions that had been exposed to intense cosmic radiations in the high Andes showed that there were *two* types of mesons; one corresponded to the Yukawa type, and the other was just the type observed by Conversi, Pancini, and Piccioni in their absorption experiments. Since 1947, there has been a very large amount of investigation of the properties and interactions of both types of mesons. Without going into details of how this work was done, we shall briefly describe the main characteristics of these mesons. In order, also, to keep abreast of the new particles that we will now be

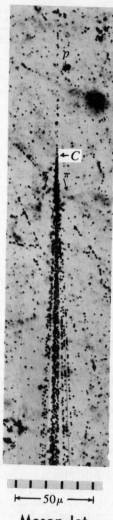

Meson Jet

In this nuclear-emulsion photograph a cosmic-ray proton p of approximately 300 Bev has collided with a stationary proton in the emulsion at C. A *jet* of 28 π mesons has been created from some of the initial energy of the incident proton. The π mesons will give rise after a short time to a secondary jet of penetrating μ mesons. (From C. F. Powell, P. H. Fowler, and D. F. Perkins, *The Study of Elementary Particles* by courtesy of Pergamon Press.)

Fundamental Particles (1962)

Class	Particle[1]	Mass[2]	Spin[3]	Stability[4]
Leptons	[5]Neutrino $\nu, \bar{\nu}$	0	Yes	Stable
	Electron $e^{\pm}$	1	Yes	Stable
	Mu meson $\mu^{\pm}$	206.8	Yes	2.2 μ sec
Mesons	Pion $\pi^{\pm}$	273.2	No	25.5 nsec
	Pion π^0	264.2	No	0.23 μnsec
	Kaon $K^+, \overline{K^+}$	966.6	No	12 nsec
	Kaon $K^0, \overline{K^0}$	974.2	No	$\begin{cases} 0.1 \text{ nsec} \\ 61 \text{ nsec} \end{cases}$
Nucleons[6]	Proton p, $\bar{p}$	1836.12	Yes	Stable
	Neutron n, $\bar{n}$	1838.65	Yes	1000 sec
Hyperons[6]	Lambda $\Lambda^0, \overline{\Lambda^0}$	2183	Yes	0.25 nsec
	Sigma $\Sigma^+, \overline{\Sigma^+}$	2328	Yes	0.08 nsec
	Sigma $\Sigma^-, \overline{\Sigma^-}$	2341	Yes	0.16 nsec
	Sigma $\Sigma^0, \overline{\Sigma^0}$	2332	Yes	Very unstable
	Xi $\Xi^-, \overline{\Xi^-}$	2580	Probably	0.13 nsec
	Xi $\Xi^0, \overline{\Xi^0}$	2566	Probably	0.15 nsec

[1] Superscript ^{0} indicates uncharged particle; superscript $+$ and $-$ indicate positively and negatively charged particles equal in magnitude to the electron's charge. A bar over a particle-symbol indicates an antiparticle. Note that $\overline{K^+} = \overline{K^-}$.

[2] As will be apparent from this column, the masses of the particles are given in units of electron mass.

[3] All particle spins, when not zero, equal one unit of spin, or $h/4\pi$. This table does not include the photon, which is a quantum of light. A photon also has spin, in this case equal to $h/2\pi$, or twice the spin of an electron. Here h is Planck's constant, defined in the Glossary. Moreover, in the expression $h/2\pi$, π is the usual symbol for the number, 3.1416, which is the ratio of the circumference of a circle to its diameter. It has no relation to the symbol $\pi^{\pm}$ or π^0 for the meson of mass approximately 270 electron masses.

[4] An isolated neutron is unstable, but a neutron bound in a stable nucleus is stable. The two lifetimes of K^0 are specially discussed in Chapter Two. The lifetime of Σ^0 has not been measured but is less than 0.01 nsec. The units of time are those used in the text: μsec (microsecond, 10^{-6}); nsec (nanosecond, 10^{-9}); μnsec (micronanosecond, 10^{-15}).

[5] Experiments (1962) indicate that there are two types of neutrinos.

[6] Nucleons and hyperons are often referred to under the comprehensive title of *baryons*, or heavy particles. For some unknown reason, the proton is a barrier that stabilizes nuclear matter.

encountering, a list of the presently known longer-lived particles is given at this time. Probably the three most essential characteristics in identifying a particle are: (1) rest mass (that is, its mass measured in the laboratory relative to which the particle is at rest), (2) spin (its inherent angular momentum, which is usually measured in terms of a quantum of spin equal to $h/4\pi$), and (3) lifetime. Concerning lifetime, we may briefly cite certain points of interest. The lifetime of a particular unstable particle is determined by the law of probabilities. We cannot predict, given only one unstable particle, how long that particular particle will live. Given a very large number of the same type of particles, we may determine an average or mean lifetime that is characteristic of the type of particles. For example, the free $\pi^\pm$ mesons have, as we have seen, a characteristic mean lifetime of 25 nanoseconds. The $\mu^\pm$ mesons have a characteristic mean lifetime of 2.2 microseconds. Masses, spins, and the mean lives of elementary particles are given in the table.

Even a physicist finds difficulty in defining the term *elementary particle*. There are many physicists who will maintain that the question is meaningless anyway. For the sake of descriptive purposes, however, the most generally accepted notion of a fundamental particle is one that, according to our present knowledge of the experimental facts, cannot be formed compositely from other more fundamental particles. By the term *formed* we mean produced in the same way as a deuteron (the nucleus of heavy hydrogen) is formed from a neutron and proton. As can be seen from the preceding table, all the presently known fundamental particles are not stable; in fact only three known particles in the table are basically stable—the neutrino, the electron, and the proton. The other fundamental particles in the table are unstable and are known to break up within characteristic time periods into other fundamental particles of smaller masses. Collected here are all the comparatively long-lived fundamental unstable particles. Even though the characteristic decay periods of these fundamental particles are short, i.e., from 2.3×10^{-16} seconds (for the π^0 meson) to 2.2×10^{-6} seconds (for the $\mu^{\pm}$ meson), there is another group of particles, which also might be called fundamental, that have lifetimes only on the order of 10^{-23} of a second. For the time being in this chapter, we shall disregard the existence of this second group of particles.

Further details of π and μ mesons

The π (pi) meson is the Yukawa meson with a mass 273 times that of the electron. The π meson exists in any of three charges—positive, negative and neutral; the magnitudes of the charges are unity in terms of the electron's charge; that is, they have the same numerical value of charge as the electron and proton. Curiously enough, the π^0 (the neutral meson) is just 9 electron masses less than the mass of the π^+ and π^- mesons. The fundamental reason for the relatively small mass differences among the π mesons is incompletely understood. There is little doubt among physicists that the differences are connected with the interactions of the charges of the positive and negative mesons with the electromagnetic field, that is, the electric and magnetic fields set up in the vacuum surrounding any electric charges or electric currents. (In order to appreciate the difficulties presented to any theory that must account for these mass differences, it is only necessary to refer to the table of elementary particles. We see that there are many apparently anomalous variations: In the π-meson family, the π^0 has less mass than the charged $\pi^{\pm}$ mesons; in the K-meson family, on the other hand, the K^0 has more mass than the charged $K^{\pm}$ mesons. There is also a small mass difference between the neutron and proton, and, in the Σ hyperons, all three particles have different masses.)

The π mesons are all unstable, and this is the reason, of course, that it took the physicists so long to find them. The

π^0 meson decays in 0.2 of a micronanosecond (2×10^{-16} sec) into two γ rays. In the perfectly free state, away from all other matter, π^+ and π^- mesons have a lifetime of 25 nanoseconds or 25 billionths of a second (25×10^{-9} sec). The π^- mesons, of course, do not live nearly this long when they pass through material substances. Because of their negative charges, they are electrically attracted to positively charged nuclei, in which they are speedily taken up by protons, just as Yukawa mesons quite properly should be! Although rather beside the point in this discussion, the effect of this absorption of a meson is usually to blow the nucleus apart into many fragment nuclei. Approximately 140 Mev (a unit of energy defined in the Glossary) are released in this explosion. The π^+ mesons, on the other hand, are repelled by positively charged nuclei and are condemned to wander about in the no-man's land between atoms until they decay of old age, in the life-span of 25 nanoseconds.

Both π^+ and π^- mesons may decay into an inert type of meson. This secondary type, which was, in fact, the first observed by Anderson and others, was called by Powell a μ (mu) meson. He observed a most interesting relationship between π and μ mesons. Those π mesons that came to rest and emitted μ mesons always produced μ mesons of exactly the same energy, namely, 4.2 Mev. The significant words in this last sentence are *always* and *exactly*. These words imply that the π meson decays into two, and only two, particles—one being the μ meson and the other being neutral (since it is not seen).

Both π- and μ-meson masses can be directly measured in ways not depending on the π-μ decay. Without going into the theoretical relativity dynamics of the decay process, it can be straightforwardly shown that the observed μ-meson energy of 4.2 Mev can only be obtained if a neutrino and a μ meson recoil back to back. The possible alternative decay into a μ meson and γ ray can be ruled out because it can be shown

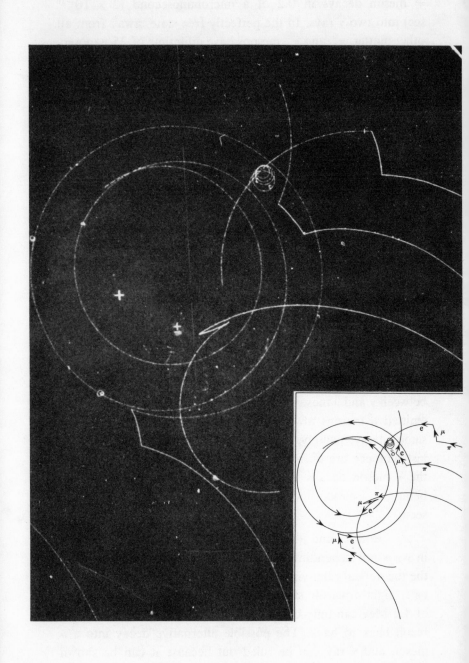

Pi-Mu-e Decays

In this bubble-chamber picture, four positively charged π mesons enter the chamber from the right and stop in the liquid hydrogen of the chamber. Each π meson then decays into a μ meson, which is observed as a short curved stub, and a neutrino, which is not observed since it is uncharged. Each of the μ mesons in turn stops, and a positively charged electron arises at the end of each μ-meson track. Three of the positive electrons (positrons) pass out of the chamber after less than half a turn, but one positron makes nearly three turns before passing out of the chamber.

It will be seen that this positron track makes tighter circles as it progresses; this is because the positron loses energy as it passes through the liquid hydrogen. All tracks are curved because the particles are moving across a magnetic field that is directed perpendicular to the plane of the photograph. All tracks curve in the same direction (since they are all from positively charged particles), except for the small δ-ray track which is a negative electron.

experimentally that a γ ray does not occur. There are also other grounds, which we need not go into, for ruling out a γ ray. In many ways, the π-μ decay is the most convincing "circumstantial" proof of the existence of the neutrino. The final balance sheet of π-meson decay is struck as follows: The observed mass of the initial π meson is 273 electron masses. The observed mass of the μ meson is 207 electron masses. The μ meson carries off an energy of 4.2 Mev, or, the mass equivalent of approximately 8 electron masses. In order to conserve both momentum and mass-energy in the π decay, the neutrino carries off a kinetic energy equivalent to the remaining 58 electron masses. This is an ample share for such a diminutive particle, but it is entirely consistent, according to relativity theory, with its zero mass!

The story of the two mesons does not end with the decay of the π meson and the birth of the μ meson. The μ meson has a comparatively long life ahead of it. By elementary-particle standards, the μ meson lives to the ripe old age of approximately 2 microseconds, or 2 millionths of a second. It then decays, in a way very reminiscent of beta decay, into an electron and two neutrinos. Why two neutrinos? Well, although only one outgoing particle (an electron) is seen from the end of a μ meson, in this case (unlike the μ meson in the π-meson decay) the outgoing electron does not always have the same amount of kinetic energy. It can be shown from conservation of energy and momentum that, if the electron recoiled against only one neutrino, it would have exactly the same energy every time. Thus it appears that the electron, in this case, recoils against at least two neutrinos and that either the directions of the neutrino recoils are not the same every time or the neutrinos do not have the same momenta each time. The maximum energy of the electron occurs when the two neutrinos fly out in the same direction and in a direction opposite to that of the electron. The observed maximum electron energy is 55 Mev. The two neutrinos are also believed to be an ordinary neutrino and an antineutrino. Surely, this is a curious state of affairs—this state in which one has ordinary matter and antimatter in particles having no matter! What is meant in this case is that the same mathematical formalism has been used to describe neutrinos as was used to describe other material particles. It is known quite definitely, as we shall see in a later chapter, that the spin properties of neutrinos and antineutrinos are quite different. It is also now known, since the Brookhaven National Laboratory experiments on neutrinos in 1962, that not only are the two neutrinos particle and antiparticle, but that they are apparently different types of neutrinos as well. This will be discussed more fully when the subject of neutrino experiments and the future of high-energy nuclear physics are taken up in Chapter Four. At this stage of

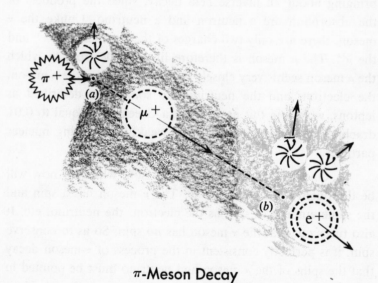

π-Meson Decay

The decay of a π meson into a μ meson and a neutrino ν has occurred at (a). The resulting μ meson may live for a few microseconds and may then decay at (b) into an electron e and two neutrinos—an ordinary ν and an anti-$\bar{\nu}$.

our story of the discovery of elementary particles and their decays, we shall merely be tantalizing and say that the ordinary neutrino emitted in μ^- decay is probably a μ-meson-associating neutrino, whereas the antineutrino is probably an electron-associating neutrino. In μ^+ decay, it is the opposite way around: the antineutrino is probably the μ-meson-associating neutrino, and the ordinary neutrino is probably the electron-associating neutrino. These seemingly complicated associations can be worked out if a principle known as the *conservation of leptons* is remembered, but we shall again defer discussion on this point.

Returning to the subject of mesons, we emphasize again that the μ meson is really quite inert. In this regard it is altogether a different "beastie," as Burns would say, from the π meson. Although the negative μ meson interacts with nuclei, its absorption by protons is slow and is to be regarded as only bringing about an inverse beta decay, since the products of the absorption are a neutron and a neutrino. Unlike the π meson, there are only two charges of the μ meson, the μ^+ and the μ^-. The μ meson is therefore like the electron, to which the μ meson seems very closely linked. As a class, the μ meson, the electron, and the neutrino are sometimes described as leptons, which, in this case, is not a Greek coin equal to 0.01 drachma but is a group of light, weakly interacting nuclear particles.

One last point about the μ meson, which by now will be thoroughly acceptable to us: The μ meson has a spin and the same amount of spin as the electron, the neutrino, etc. It also turns out that the π meson has *no* spin. So as to conserve spin, it is perfectly consistent in the process of π-meson decay that the spins of the μ meson and neutrino must be pointed in opposite directions when the two particles are produced. Thus, if we have already accepted the argument that the neutrino has spin, there is no way out of also accepting the fact that the μ meson has the same amount of spin. We should also add, for the sake of completeness, that a π meson can decay, in a rather infrequent number of cases, directly into an electron and a neutrino. This decay, one should also note, conserves spin of the π meson, too. The nature of the grand design, especially relating to the niche occupied by the μ meson, is a wide-open question at this time (1962).

Discovery of the strange particles

When World War II ended, one of the first laboratories to start up basic nuclear research again was that at the University of Manchester under the inspiring directorship of Blackett. An important project carried out was an analysis of cosmic rays using large, Wilson cloud chambers. Blackett, himself, had already made many important contributions in the field of low-energy physics using cloud chambers, and it was not long before two of his associates, Rochester and Butler, discovered that very unusual particles were turning up in their cosmic-ray pictures. They saw a type of particle which they called a V particle because, simply, the tracks were in the form of a vee with the point generally at the top of the chamber. We shall not try to trace the history of the next 5 years or so after the first discovery of V particles. In many ways one might describe the situation as rather chaotic. New particles were reported from many different laboratories all over the world. However, because their numbers were counted in ones and twos, it was difficult to coordinate and assemble the data.

As an instance of the paucity of the events and, yet, as a demonstration of the essential certainty of the data, the case of the first τ (tau) particle found by Powell and the Bristol nuclear-emulsion group in 1949 can be cited. This event was found in photographic emulsions that had been exposed to cosmic rays. The event consisted of the track of a particle that came to a full stop in the emulsion and then decayed into three undeniable π-meson tracks, all of which were in the same plane. There could be no interpretation other than of a particle that had come to rest and had decayed into three and *only* three π mesons. The mass of the initial particle could, therefore, be accurately obtained from the masses of the π mesons, which were then known, and the energies of the π mesons, which were observed in this event. The mass turned out to be accurately 964 times that of the electron mass. Although the mass obtained by direct observation on the track was not as accurate as this, it nevertheless agreed with this value. For 2 years this event was the only example of its kind, yet the

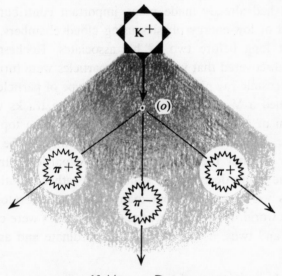

K-Meson Decay

One of the ways in which a K meson decays is the so-called τ mode. A τ meson is here shown decaying into three charged π mesons at (o). It will be seen that three charges have risen from the one charge of the K⁺ meson. In the balance, however, this is consistent, since two of the π meson charges are positive and one π meson charge is negative.

~ 40 ~

completeness of the decay and the accuracy of the mass determination were such that the existence of this type of particle could never have been in doubt. (The τ meson today is known to be merely one of the alternative decay modes of a charged K meson.)

Two broad classes of particles had become recognized toward the end of the 1947 to 1952 period; all this work depended upon the natural cosmic-ray source of new particles. There were those particles that became known as K particles, with masses heavier than π and μ mesons yet lighter than protons and neutrons. There were also particles whose masses were greater than those of protons and neutrons; these new extra-heavy particles became known as hyperons. Although the main features of K particles and hyperons were obtained in broad outline using cosmic-ray sources, the details were rapidly filled in after 1953 when operation of the first billion-electric-volt accelerators at Brookhaven and Berkeley began. The "strange particles," namely, K particles and hyperons, will now be briefly described.

Extraordinary schizophrenia of neutral K particle

There are three charges of K particles, corresponding to positive, negative, and zero charges. Like π mesons, K particles also possess no spin. Both the K^+ and K^- particles may decay in a number of different ways: (1) to three π mesons, (2) to two π mesons, (3) to a μ meson and a neutrino, and (4) to a π^0 meson, a μ meson, and a neutrino (ν) or to an electron, a π^0 meson, and a neutrino. The charged K particles have an average lifetime of approximately 12 nanoseconds, that is, about the same lifetime as the charged π mesons. The neutral K particle, on the other hand, has an extraordinary Jekyll-and-Hyde existence. The K_1^0, or the Mr. Hyde character, has quick decay in 0.1 nanosecond. This decay results in a π^+ and a π^- meson and was the decay first observed by Rochester and

Butler. They called this particle the V_1^0 because the two π mesons produced in the decay formed a vee. The π mesons are hurled forward and outward into a vee when a K_1^0 decays in flight. The K_2^0, or the Dr. Jekyll character, has a slower decay —61 nanoseconds. This decay is into three particles, either (1) three π mesons, (2) one π meson, a μ meson, and a neutrino, or (3) one π meson, an electron, and a neutrino. This observed schizophrenia of the K^0 particle spectacularly confirmed another of those brilliant predictions that have become associated with this almost "magic" era of quantum mechanics. Gell-Mann and Pais started from the viewpoint that an ordinary K^0 particle could not be identical with an antimatter $\overline{K}^0$ because, experimentally, the particles showed no tendency to be produced equally in certain types of production reactions. (By way of comparison, we should point out that there is only one π^0 meson—both the ordinary π^0 meson and the anti-π^0 meson are identical.) Gell-Mann and Pais, who were then both at the Institute for Advanced Study in Princeton, predicted that there should be two different neutral particles, the K_1^0 and the K_2^0, which we have just discussed. It is to these two K particles that the difference between K^0 and $\overline{K}^0$ is attributed. They predicted that the K_1^0 and K_2^0 would be produced in equal numbers in a reaction, would possess different decay lifetimes, and would even have slightly different masses. Moreover, it was subsequently predicted that a beam of seemingly pure K_2^0 particles would again be convertible to a mixture of K_1^0 and K_2^0 simply by passing the K_2^0 beam through matter. To explain what this means experimentally, consider a beam of K^0 particles emerging from the target of some high-energy accelerator. In the first few centimeters of flight path, one finds predominantly the rapid two-pi decay, but after a few centimeters only the slower three-pi decay is observed. This is naturally interpreted as evidence that the original beam was a mixture of K_1^0 and K_2^0 in which most of the K_1^0 particles decayed in a few tenths of a nanosecond, and the K_2^0 particles were still left after as much as 61 nanoseconds and more. However, if, after 61 nanoseconds, the beam is passed through a centimeter or two of metal plate, one can again observe particles having the two-pi decays emerging from the metal plate. Owing to their interactions with the nuclei of the metal, some of the K_2^0 particles of the beam have been changed into a mixture of K_1^0 and K_2^0 again. This is explicable if both K^0 and $\overline{K}^0$ particles are mixtures of K_1^0 and K_2^0.

Distinguishing features of the hyperons

It is, of course, hazardous to suggest that anything in science is a closed book. In the strange-particle business, as it stands today (1962), there is still only one long-lived K-particle group, and there are only three long-lived hyperon groups. (For discussion of the qualification *long-lived*, see the earlier note on the fundamental particles in this chapter.) There have been a number of alarms in the last 5 years but no new group has been added in this time. The three hyperon groups are: the Λ (lambda) hyperon, the Σ (sigma) hyperons, and the Ξ (Xi) hyperons.

The Λ particle is neutral and has a mass of 2183 electron masses. It is also one of the original vee particles, the so-called V_2^0. Its vee-like appearance in a cloud chamber arises from its decay products—a π^- meson and a proton. An alternative decay of the Λ^0 is into a π^0 meson and a neutron. Its average lifetime is approximately ¼ nanosecond. Occasionally the Λ^0 has been observed to decay into a proton, an electron, and a neutrino.

There are three Σ hyperons, corresponding to the three states of positive, negative, and zero charges. They have been found to possess slightly different masses, but, from the nature of their decays, they all clearly belong to the same group of particles. The Σ^0 mass of 2332 electron masses is representative of the Σ group. The Σ^+ hyperon decays in approximately

0.1 nanosecond into either a proton and a π^0 meson or into a neutron and a π^+ meson. The Σ^- hyperon decays in approximately 0.2 nanosecond into a neutron and a π^- meson. The Σ^0 hyperon decays in an as yet undetermined short time into a Λ^0 and γ ray.

The Ξ hyperon, which is sometimes referred to as a cascade particle, was for many years (even after high-energy machines had been in operation), known only from cosmic rays. The negatively charged Ξ hyperon decays in approxi-

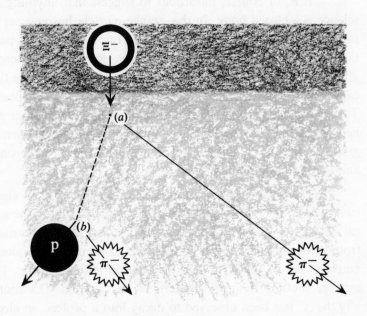

Ξ^- Hyperon Decay

A Ξ^- hyperon is here shown to decay at (a) into a π^- meson and a Λ^0 hyperon. The path of the Λ^0 between (a) and (b) is dotted, since this hyperon, being neutrally charged, will not be seen. At (b), the Λ^0 hyperon is shown to decay into a proton p and a π^- meson.

Because of the double decay of the Ξ^- hyperon, this particle was initially known as the *cascade particle*.

mately 0.1 nanosecond into a Λ^0 hyperon and a π^- meson. The Λ^0 subsequently decays, hence the *cascade* appearance of the Ξ^- decay. The Ξ^0 hyperon decays, with approximately the same lifetime as the Ξ^-, into a Λ^0 and a π^0. The Ξ hyperons are the most massive fundamental particles presently known. It is significant that no positively charged Ξ hyperon has been observed. Like the neutron and proton, all hyperons have a spin, and they also possess antiparticle counterparts.

"Strangeness"—a peculiar property

Like pi-mesons, strange particles can be produced by the bombardment of protons, neutrons, mesons, or γ rays on either neutrons or protons. Despite the fact that strange particles are readily produced, beams of strange particles that are passed through matter decay rather slowly. Since ready production implies strong interaction with atomic nuclei, whereas slow decay implies weak interaction, we find ourselves with a dilemma. It was this precise dilemma that Pais resolved in 1952 with the proposition that strange particles are always produced in pairs.

In practice, the so-called principle of *associated production* proposed by Pais means that an ordinary K particle or an ordinary hyperon must be produced together with its antiparticle or, alternatively, that an ordinary K particle must be produced in association with an ordinary hyperon. An anti-K particle will be associated with an antihyperon but not with an ordinary hyperon. However, this is not yet all! The Ξ hyperon, if not accompanied by its anti-Ξ hyperon, must be associated with no less than two K particles. If there is any fundamental reason why some particles are *strange* and others not, it escapes us at present.

Unless associated particles manage to locate one another after production, which is, of course, completely improbable, their decay is a comparatively slow process. The

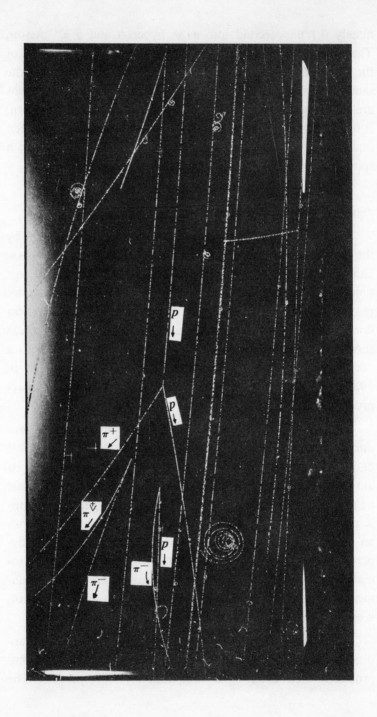

K^0 and Λ^0 Production

In this bubble-chamber picture, many 2.85-Bev protons are seen to enter the chamber from the top and curve slightly toward the left under the action of a magnetic field that is directed perpendicular to the plane of the picture. One of the protons is seen to strike a stationary proton in the liquid hydrogen of the chamber. At the point of collision, a π^+ meson and proton track fork apart. Also at this point a Λ^0 hyperon and a K^0 meson are simultaneously produced: So-called associated production.

The K^0 meson moves forward and subsequently decays into a π^+ and a π^- meson. The Λ^0 also moves forward and subsequently decays into a π^- meson and a proton.

suggestion that the slow decay was related to another property, called isotopic spin, was first put forward by Peaslee, but a most imaginative and complete phenomenological theory was first developed by Gell-Mann and Nishijima in 1953. According to this theory, which has been consistent with observations up to the present day (1962), fundamental particles can be assigned *strangeness* numbers. In a strong interaction, such as a production process of strange particles, strangeness is conserved; that is, the sum of the strangeness numbers on the left-hand side of the reaction is equal to the sum of the strangeness numbers of the particles on the right-hand side. In a weak interaction, however, such as the decay of a strange particle, strangeness is not conserved, and it is believed that, in some way, the fact that the strangeness has to change slows down the pace of the reaction.

In accordance with the scheme of Gell-Mann and Nishijima, the strangeness numbers given as follows have been assigned to the elementary particles described in this chapter:

$$\text{strangeness} \quad 0: \quad \pi^+, \pi^0, \pi^-, \text{n}, \text{p}, \bar{\text{n}}, \bar{\text{p}}$$
$$\text{strangeness} \quad 1: \quad \text{K}^+, \text{K}^0, \overline{\Lambda^0}, \overline{\Sigma^+}, \overline{\Sigma^0}, \overline{\Sigma^-}$$
$$\text{strangeness} -1: \quad \overline{\text{K}^+}, \overline{\text{K}^0}, \Lambda^0, \Sigma^+, \Sigma^0, \Sigma^-$$
$$\text{strangeness} \quad 2: \quad \overline{\Xi^0}, \overline{\Xi^-}$$
$$\text{strangeness} -2: \quad \Xi^0, \Xi^-$$

Leptons are generally assigned no strangeness numbers.

As illustrations of applications of the strangeness concept to strange-particle physics we give the following few examples:

(1) Allowed associated production

$$\pi^- + \text{p} \rightarrow \Lambda^0 + \text{K}^0$$
$$0 + 0 = -1 + 1$$

i.e., strangeness balances

(2) Not-allowed associated production

$$n + n \rightarrow \Lambda^0 + \Lambda^0$$
$$0 + 0 \neq -1 + (-1)$$

i.e., strangeness does not balance

(3) Slow decay allowed

$$K_1^0 \rightarrow \pi^+ + \pi^-$$
$$1 \neq 0 + 0$$

Fast decay not allowed; strangeness does not balance

Only since the recent discovery of the strange particle has one further principle of nuclear reactions been recognized —namely, the principle of the conservation of baryons. As we have already mentioned, all baryons ultimately revert to protons, which have been found to possess long-term stability. The stability is also reflected in nuclear reactions, for it is found that the number of baryons on the left-hand side of a reaction always equals the number of baryons on the right-hand side of the reaction. For instance, this is borne out by the reaction equations used to illustrate the strangeness concept above. There is one minor complication—what happens when there are antibaryons? For example, an antiproton and a proton annihilate to give no baryons at all, only pi mesons. For the purpose of considering the conservation of baryons, we must count an antibaryon as a negative-unity baryon; the algebraic sum of baryons and antibaryons on the left-hand side of a reaction will then always equal the similar sum of baryons on the right-hand side of the equation.

Deeper questions involved with fundamental particles

Powell, Nobel Laureate in 1950, said: "In the years which have passed, the study of what might, in the early days,

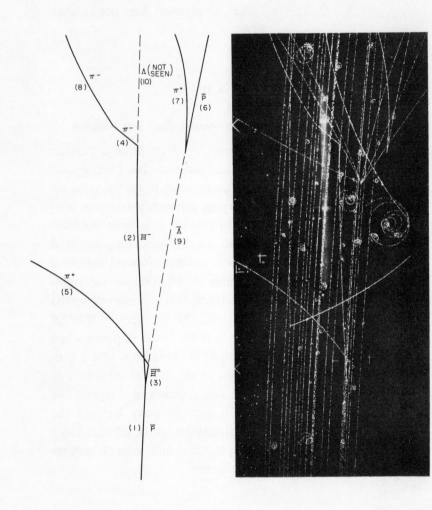

Ξ and Anti-Ξ Particles

This bubble-chamber photograph shows the production of a Ξ^- hyperon (track 2) and an anti-Ξ^--hyperon (track 3), denoted by $\overline{\Xi^-}$. (Notice that the $\overline{\Xi^-}$ is the same as $\overline{\Xi}^+$). These two strange particles were produced by a 3-Bev antiproton (track 1, denoted by $\overline{P}$) colliding with an ordinary proton in the liquid hydrogen of the bubble chamber. The subsequent decays of the Ξ^- and $\overline{\Xi^-}$ are seen in the chamber. $\overline{\Xi^-}$ decays to π^+ and $\overline{\Lambda^0}$ (thus conserving the single positive charge possessed by the $\overline{\Xi^-}$), and Ξ^- decays to π^- and Λ^0. In the case of the antilambda hyperon $\overline{\Lambda^0}$ (track 9, which is not seen in the chamber because of the particle's zero charge) the cascade decay is seen into π^+ and antiproton $\overline{P}$ (tracks 7 and 6, respectively).

Several other extraneous details of bubble-chamber art are also apparent in the picture. Just between and below the two vertices of tracks 4, 10 and tracks 7, 6 a fan of six slightly curved tracks can be seen. These probably represent six π mesons emerging from an annihilation of an antiproton with a proton. (The beam entering the bottom of the picture is preponderantly antiprotons).

Just to the left of track 5 is observed a collision between an antiproton, which is in the beam, and an ordinary proton, which was in the liquid; this is very similar to a collision that occurs between billiard balls, and the dynamics are much the same. A number of curled tracks are also to be seen in the picture. These are slow electrons that are curved because a magnetic field is being impressed on the bubble chamber and charged particles are bent in it. The electron tracks spiral inward because the electrons lose energy as they traverse the liquid hydrogen. It will be noticed that the outward arms of the spirals always start in the direction of the top of the picture. This is because the electrons are projected from atoms in the collisions always in the direction of the beam particles.

have been regarded as trivial phenomena has, in fact, led us to the discovery of many new forms of matter and many new processes of fundamental physical importance. It has contributed to the development of a picture of the material universe as a system in a state of perpetual change and flux . . . We are only at the beginning of our penetration into what appears to be a rich field of discovery. Already, however, it seems certain that our present theoretical approach has been limited by lack of essential information and that the world of mesons is far more complex than has hitherto been visualized in the most brilliant theoretical speculations." One feels that the situation in 1962 is still much as Powell spoke of it in 1950. Where all the particles, which we have discussed in this chapter, fit into the scheme of things is still a great challenge for the physicist.

Although no fundamental theory of elementary particles has yet been given, certain features stand out and may form the basis of preliminary classifications. One scheme of classification can be built along the lines of the so-called *strengths* of interactions. This property describes the intensity of the forces that act between particles when they are associated in some kind of particle interaction, such as the production of particles or the decay of particles. Those interactions between particles that are described as *strong* usually occur within very short times [on the order of a hundred thousand billion billionth of a second (10^{-23} second)]. Most nuclear-production processes are characterized by such short time periods. An organization chart of the particles which can interact strongly is shown. This diagram is divided by a central dashed line into two halves. Ordinary particles are represented on one side of the diagram, and antiparticles are on the opposite side. The two halves are, as it were, mirror images of one another and are alike in all respects except that the signs of one-half are opposite to the signs of the other half: both the signs of the electrical charges and the signs of the strangeness numbers are reversed. (Note that a symbol with a bar, such as $\overline{K}^-$, is an antiparticle, in this case of K^+.)

A gamma ray or a photon is not considered to be a strongly interacting particle because it takes part only in electromagnetic interactions, which are, in fact, about 100 times weaker than the strong nuclear and elementary-particle interactions. However, because a gamma ray may take part in

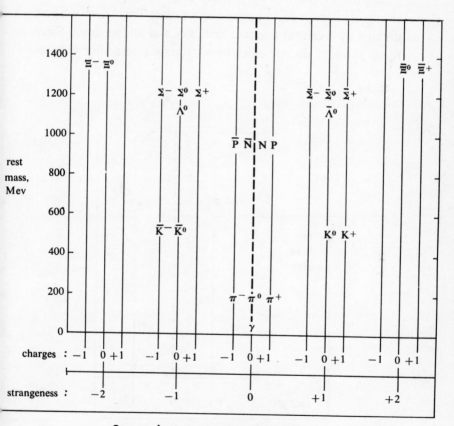

Strongly Interacting Particles

Organization chart of the strongly interacting particles.

reactions involving strange particles, it is assigned a strangeness number, which turns out to be zero.

The strongly interacting particles may also take part in slow or weak interactions. However, some particles (termed the weakly interacting particles) only take part in comparatively long-period reactions. Characteristically, it is the weakly interacting particles that are associated with decays of most elementary particles. The strengths of the weak interactions are some 10-million-million times weaker than the strong interactions. A chart of the weakly interacting particles is also shown. It is seen to comprise the leptons. This chart is again divided by a central line into ordinary and antiparticles. Since these particles do not enter into strongly interacting strange-

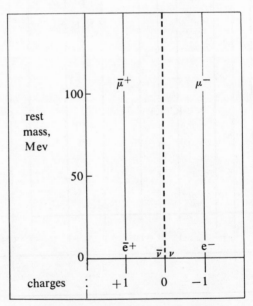

Weakly Interacting Particles

Organization chart of the weakly interacting particles.

particle-production processes, no assignment of strangeness number is made.

In Chapter One we noted that ordinary matter and antimatter particles were predicted by Dirac. The implication from Dirac's theory is that nature is symmetrical with regard to charge, or that the microscopic laws of physics are *invariant* for both particle and antiparticle. (In Chapter Four, we shall note briefly that this statement must be regarded as no longer true for weak interactions.) The particular invariance that Dirac built into his theory was *relativistic invariance,* or the independence of physical laws on the velocity of an observer. This invariance is basic to Einstein's theory of special relativity, the same well-established theory that predicted the equivalence of mass and energy. Many other symmetries have also been noted, and theories of their origins in other invariance properties of nature have been proposed. It will be observed, for instance, in the organization charts of fundamental particles, that certain particles form small subgroups: nucleons n and p; pi mesons π^+, π^0, and π^-; Σ hyperons Σ^+, Σ^0, and Σ^-; etc. These subgroups are referred to as multiplets, and theoretical physicists regard members of a multiplet as arising from a number of symmetrical orientations of an *isotopic spin.* What the properties of space, time, mass, or nature are, which determine isotopic-spin values, is not known. Just as in the case of strangeness, assignments of isotopic spins can be given to all the elementary particles. It can be shown that the conservation of strangeness, in K particle and hyperon production, for example, is related to conservation of a part (one of the orientations) of the isotopic spin of the particles occurring in the reaction. Isotopic-spin conservation, however, does not remain valid in the field of weak interactions. At the present time, this type of failure is the primary difficulty with the postulate that invariance properties underlie the origins of the many fundamental particles observed in high-energy physics today. Many other attempts, both highly imaginative and very abstract, have also been directed at explaining the origins of

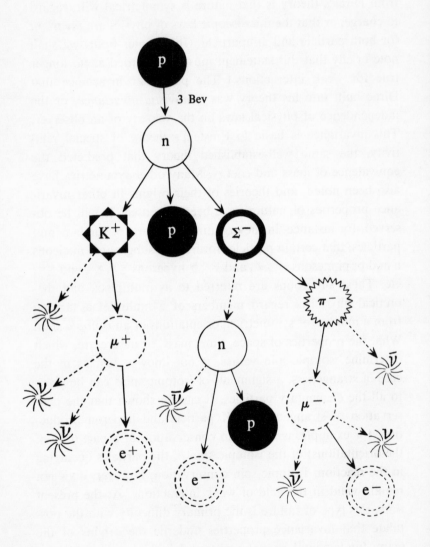

K^+ and Σ^- Production

A cascade of particles may be produced by the collision of a high-energy proton (e.g., 3 Bev) against a neutron. Two strange particles, a K^+ and Σ^- are produced, together with one of the protons remaining. In this reaction, some of the 3 Bev of energy has gone into producing the two new particles. Note, however, that the number of baryons has been conserved. At any stage, the total energy of mass and energy is also conserved. Following through the various decays, many of which are alternatives, the end products are two protons, two negative electrons and one positive electron, and seven neutrinos. The positive electron will subsequently annihilate with a negative electron and γ radiation will result. The sum total of changes will therefore bring back the original particles (since, if the neutron had been free, it would have decayed into a proton and an electron). The initial energy of the proton projectile has largely been transformed into neutrino energy, γ radiation, and a certain amount of kinetic energy still remains with the protons and electrons.

the fundamental particles, which have been outlined in this chapter. As of this time, however, no theory has received even partial acceptance, and the nature of the design underlying the particles still remains one of the great scientific challenges of the twentieth century.

three

MACHINES OF
NUCLEAR PHYSICS

"The possession of the world's highest energy accelerator is, and always has been, a transitory state . . . ," wrote Adams, Director General of the European Organization for Nuclear Research (CERN), in 1960, when Western Europe had short-lived possession of the highest-energy accelerator for the first time in 20 years. Although wonders of the world are always being eclipsed, it would not seem too bold to claim one giant accelerator of the early 1960s as a select member of the engineering wonders of the twentieth century. As the first years of the 1960s opened, two accelerators, one at Geneva built by the European collaborative group, CERN, and one at Brookhaven built by the Associated Universities Incorporated for the U.S. Atomic Energy Commission, reached the proton energy of approximately 30 billion (or giga) electron volts $(3 \times 10^{10}$ ev). To appreciate these large accelerators of the 1960s, it is first necessary to say a little about their very modest beginning some 30 years earlier.

First accelerators

Until the 1920s, except for x-ray machines producing hundreds of thousands of volts, physicists in Rutherford's day had to use energetic radioactivity particles for their experiments. The first disintegrations of atomic nuclei were observed

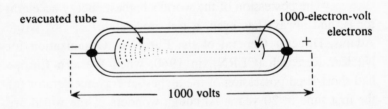

Accelerating-Gap Principle

If a 1000-volt battery is connected across an evacuated glass tube with two electrodes, as indicated in this diagram, electrons will be accelerated across the gap and will reach the other side with an energy of 1000 electron volts. In an x-ray tube, for instance, electrons are generally supplied at the negative (—) end by an incandescent filament. Unless the glass tube is evacuated, the electrons will collide with gas atoms as they move across the gap. For an electron to achieve full 1000 ev, it must start at one end and traverse the whole gap without having a collision.

in 1919 by Rutherford, who fired alpha particles from radium C at nitrogen nuclei. The highest-energy alpha, or helium, particles, which were available from naturally occurring radioactive substances for the first "splitting-the-atom" experiments, were approximately 8 million electron volts. A million electron volts, or Mev, is a measure of energy gained by either an electron, proton, or any other unit-charge particle when it is speeded up across the entire gap between electrodes connected to 1 million volts. In the late 1920s, many experimenters were working on methods of producing the millions of volts necessary for accelerating ionized particles such as protons. Two physicists, Cockcroft and Walton, working at the University of Cambridge under the eager eyes of the first smasher of atoms, Rutherford himself, invented an electronic, voltage-multiplying circuit for building up a voltage of 700,000 volts. It is now part of scientific history that, in response to Rutherford's cheerful challenge, they gave their atom smasher a try at 400,000 volts, half the desired voltage, and were rewarded by being the first in history to split an atom by artificially accelerated nuclear particles.

Another ingenious electrical, high-voltage generator was being developed at this time by Van de Graaff. His device was really a sophisticated elaboration of a well-known schoolboy fascination of electrically charging a plastic comb or pen by rubbing it on hair or fur. In the Van de Graaff generator, a revolving belt transfers such electrostatic charges to a large, insulated-metal storage sphere. Very high voltages can be built up in this fashion, and they can then be applied to a long, evacuated-glass tube in which gaseous charged particles, such as protons, may be accelerated.

Protons reaching energies of as high as 15 Mev have been accelerated through the use of Van de Graaff generators, and a prodigious amount of low-energy nuclear-physics research has already been produced using these machines.

Cockcroft-Walton Accelerator

Cockcroft-Walton accelerator for 800 kilovolts. This generator supplies voltage for the pre-injector of protons into a 30-Mev linear accelerator, which is, in turn, the injector into the 30-Bev alternating-gradient synchrotron at Brookhaven National Laboratory.

In brief, a Cockcroft-Walton generator operates by taking high voltages from an alternating-current transformer and by rectifying and multiplying these voltages by an ingenious arrangement of tubes and capacitors.

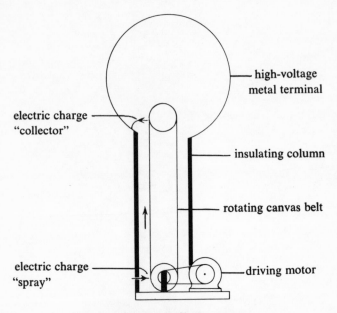

electric charge "collector"

high-voltage metal terminal

insulating column

rotating canvas belt

electric charge "spray"

driving motor

Van de Graaff Generator

In the Van de Graaff generator, charges can be sprayed on to a cloth belt which then transports the charges to a large, collecting-high-voltage-metal sphere supported on an insulating-material cylinder. The charges leave the belt by way of fine metal points arranged on a comb placed very close to the surface of the moving belt. Once on the metal comb, they "run" immediately to the outside surface of the metal sphere, which then forms the electrode of an accelerating tube usually standing alongside the generator.

The voltage developed on the collecting sphere is limited by the rate of mechanical transfer of the electric charge on the belt and by the leakage discharge through the air to the surroundings. In later models of Van de Graaff generators, the leakage discharge is reduced by enclosing the whole apparatus in a tank containing inert gas under pressure.

Development of circular accelerators

With the two high-voltage generators and particle accelerators just discussed there are two serious difficulties in going to higher energies. First, high voltages are easier to generate than to tame. High-voltage spark-over causes damage and loss of voltage and stability. (In order to prevent some spark-over, the latest Van de Graaff generators are enclosed in high-pressure, inert-gas-filled containers.) The second difficulty is that there are practical limits to the length of the tubes that can directly withstand the voltages for accelerating the charged particles.

The cyclotron principle of charged-particle acceleration, which was invented by Lawrence at the University of California, Berkeley, in 1932, overcame both of these difficulties. It has been the basic principle underlying most of the large accelerators used today. Not only was Lawrence the inventor of this type of machine but he was also the inventor of a way of life, which is often referred to as *Berkelitis*. This attitude is a bold and large-scale approach toward solving the problems of physics.

The cyclotron principle is to give many small acceleration pulses to the charged particles as they are led around a circular path. Basically, the principal of constant-frequency pulses depends on the fact that the time for a complete circular revolution of a charged particle in a constant magnetic field is a constant. In other words, although the particle may gain speed as it gains energy, the time it takes to go around a circular path is a constant, because the size of the circle is just that much bigger for the higher energy. A final voltage of, say 10 Mev, is achieved by particles accelerated by 500 pulses when 20,000 electron volts are gained on each pulse. The speed of a high-energy particle is very high. For instance, a proton of 4.7 Mev has a velocity equal to one-tenth the

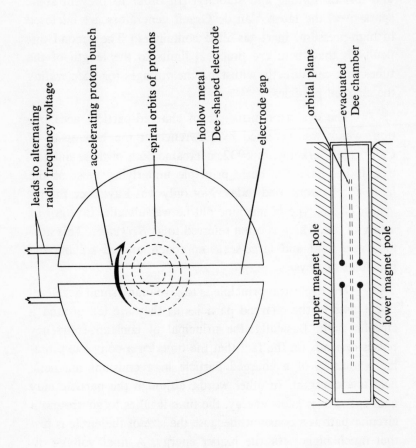

leads to alternating
radio frequency voltage

accelerating proton bunch

spiral orbits of protons

hollow metal
Dee-shaped electrode

electrode gap

orbital plane

evacuated
Dee chamber

upper magnet pole

lower magnet pole

Lawrence Cyclotron

In the Lawrence cyclotron, protons circulate in a spiral orbit in a horizontal plane lying midway between the poles of a magnet. The spiral moves further out on each transit of the protons across the electrode gap. However, the time necessary to describe a half-circle of orbit is the same no matter which part of the spiral the proton is on.

It is this property of the cyclotron which enables a constant-frequency acceleration to be used. On each half-circular turn of a proton bunch, the direction of polarity of the electric accelerating field across the electrode gap is reversed by the alternating-radiofrequency supply to which the electrode dees are connected.

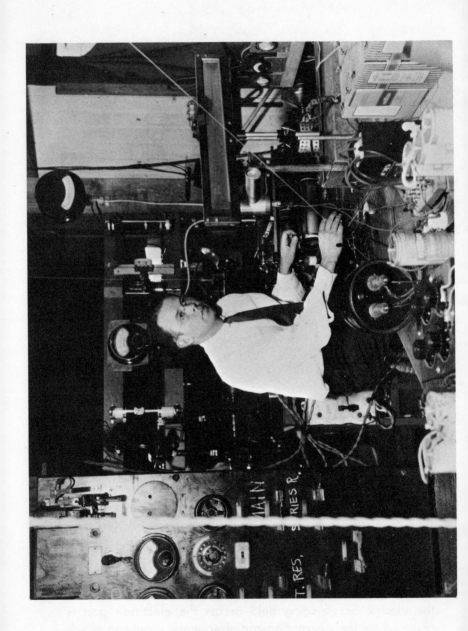

velocity of light c, which, incidentally, is 30 billion centimeters per second or 186,000 miles per second. A proton of 1.3 Bev is moving at nine-tenths of c; a proton of 5 Bev, ninety-nine hundredths of c. With very high frequency pulsing, therefore, such as will be produced from a radiofrequency oscillator of, say, 10 million cycles per second, it may take only 250 circular turns or only 25 microseconds for a proton to reach an energy of 10 million electron volts. Toward the end of the 1930s, cyclotrons were providing the most-intense and highest-energy sources of nuclear particles available, either naturally or artificially. In this time in the United States alone there were probably as many as 10 separate installations in operation or under construction, and it was primarily around these machines that the measurements of important constants required in the design of nuclear explosives and reactors were made during the war. However, grave doubts were appearing at this stage that the cyclotron principle of acceleration could be extended to quite high energies.

It appeared as though there might be a practical limit to the energy of protons at about 20 Mev. The argument went as follows: As a nuclear particle speeds up, its mass also increases. This is known as the relativistic mass increase, because it was first described by Einstein in his theory of special relativity. At all low velocities, such as those we are accus-

E. O. Lawrence

E. O. Lawrence at the controls of the 27-inch-diameter cyclotron. This was the second cyclotron constructed at the Radiation Laboratory, University of California, Berkeley, and it produced 5-Mev deuterons in 1934.

tomed to in normal, everyday phenomena, this increase of mass is negligible. Even the velocities of the fastest rockets and satellites are insignificant compared with the velocity of light. For these nuclear-high-energy particles, however, it is highly significant. Today, the high-energy physicists have utmost confidence in the validity of the special theory of relativity. They have learned that only the strictest attention to relativity theory —and not merely to Newton's classical mechanics, which is exact only at low velocities—will describe collisions between high-energy nuclear particles. Experience also has shown that only the utmost reliance on relativity theory will enable the designer of high-energy machines to achieve the correct trajectories of charged particles in his machines.

To illustrate how significant the mass change is, let us look at the values for a proton of the energies already considered. The mass of a proton moving at one-tenth the velocity of light c is one-half of a per cent greater than that of a proton at rest; at ninth-tenths of c, the proton mass is 2.37 times its rest mass; and at ninety-nine hundredths of c, its mass is 6.3 times its rest mass. In a cyclotron, if the masses of accelerated particles increase significantly as their energies rise, this means that they will move more slowly than they would have moved if their masses had remained constant. We have seen that the cyclotron principle is dependent on a constant period of revolution, and it holds accurately only for particles that retain constant mass. If the constant periodicity of the particle is broken, the correct phasing (as it is called) or timing of the accelerating pulses is thrown out of synchronism. Since the timing of the acceleration pulses in the then-existing cyclotrons could not afford to be out of synchronism with the particles by more than about 1 per cent or, cumulatively, by about one-quarter of a turn, it is little wonder that a halt was called on extending cyclotrons to higher energies, at least before having a further look at the difficulties suggested by relativity.

Cyclotron Model

In this mechanical model of the cyclotron, a ball is released from the center source tube S once every complete revolution of the balls, which keep in line throughout their whole motion, as shown in the picture. Acceleration of the balls occurs only when they cross the diametral rectangular strip, AB.

This is accomplished by producing a tilt in the strip just as the balls reach its edge. The tilt is produced by raising or lowering one semicircular part of the track, relative to the other part, by means of a mechanical rocker.

Even though the outer balls achieve higher velocities, they nevertheless arrive at the accelerating strips, because of their longer orbits around the outer tracks, at approximately the same times as the inner balls. Some lagging behind of the outer balls does occur, presumably because of relatively larger frictional effects on these balls. This lagging may be likened to a relativistic-mass effect that occurs for particles accelerated in cyclotrons. (This photograph of a working exhibit is reproduced by permission of the Director of the Science Museum, London.)

Circular machines—
extension to Bev energies

In the cyclotron, the relativistic increase of mass at higher energies at the end of the acceleration causes the particles to lag more and more behind the accelerating pulses. In the beginning 1940s, two physicists, McMillan at Berkeley and Veksler in Moscow, both suggested changing the frequency of the accelerating pulses to keep in step with the circulating particles. This idea was soon put into operation at Berkeley with that despatch for which Lawrence's laboratory was famous. This machine, which was called a synchro-cyclotron, extended by more than 1 order of magnitude the energy of its predecessor and produced protons of 350 Mev. Similar machines were later built at Chicago (U.S.A.), Liverpool (England), Dubna (U.S.S.R.), and Geneva (Switzerland). Another suggestion for overcoming the relativistic limitation of the cyclotron was made by Oliphant, who was at that time professor of physics at the University of Birmingham in England. His idea was to change both the time of circulation of the protons in their orbits and the timing of the accelerating pulses in such a way that all the orbits were in a circular ring of approximately the same radius. This is quite a different kind of circulation from that occurring in the cyclotron, where the protons start from a center and circulate in ever-increasing spiral paths toward the edge of the machine. A certain experimental finesse was needed to achieve acceleration in this new machine because it required changes of two quantities in order to synchronize the particles with the pulses. The name given to this type of accelerator was the *synchrotron,* and, because the largest machines of the 1950s and early 1960s are of this type, a fuller description of one of them will be given. Designs for three proton synchrotrons, in the billion- or thousand-million-electron-volt class, were independently laid down in the same period of the middle 1940s. A 1-Bev accelerator was planned

High-Energy Particles

The first "extracted" beam of high-energy particles from a cyclotron—this experiment was performed by E. M. McMillan at Berkeley, in 1936. The particles are deuterons of approximately 5 Mev. They are seen in the photograph because of the ionization they cause in the oxygen and nitrogen of the air. All the high-energy particles have about the same "range" in air because they have the same initial energy and the air offers the same degradation of energy to each particle.

in Oliphant's laboratory in England; a 3-Bev accelerator, called the *cosmotron* was projected at the Brookhaven National Laboratory in Long Island, U.S.A.; and designs for a 6-Bev machine called the *bevatron* were made at the University of California, Berkeley. The first of these to produce a beam "for the enlightenment and benefit of mankind" was the cosmotron in 1952.

Brookhaven Cosmotron Section

This quarter-scale model of a section of the Brookhaven cosmotron shows the way in which the acceleration chamber C fits into the horizontal slot of magnet block M. At the left is a view of the vacuum pump V, which removes gas from the acceleration chamber via a junction vessel J.

In the cosmotron, protons are guided around a race-track path consisting of 4 quadrants and 4 straight sections joined together in a ring of approximately 30 feet radius. The quadrant sections are formed from octagonal-shaped, ½-inch-thick iron plates stacked vertically together. A horizontal slot, to contain the vacuum chamber in which the protons circulate, is cut in the outside edge of the magnet plates. The weight of the magnet is 2000 tons. The protons are guided, inside the vacuum chamber, by means of a magnetic field that bends the protons into an approximately fixed-circular path of 30-foot radius. In the 4 straight sections, there is no magnetic field, and the protons travel straight from one quadrant section to the next. As the velocity of the protons rises, so the guiding magnetic field must be increased in order to maintain the protons in a fixed orbit. The magnetic field is produced by coils that are wound around the iron plates and that carry large currents from an electric generator. In order to increase the magnetic field to the peak value of 14,000 gauss at the end of the acceleration period, the current through the magnetic coils must be increased from 0 to a value of 7000 amperes. The increase of current occurs in approximately 1 second, which is the normal acceleration time of the protons. In this time, the protons, traveling in a bunch something like a flock of birds, will have gone a distance of about 200,000 kilometers, approximately 3 million times around the machine, or 5 times around the earth. In order to supply the large current to the magnet over such a long period as 1 second, a large amount of energy must be stored. The method chosen was to store the energy in the form of mechanical energy, namely, as rotational kinetic energy, in a 45-ton flywheel linked directly to the shaft of the electric generator rotor. The energy stored in the fly-wheel at peak is 1.7×10^7 joules. This is the equivalent of approximately 22,500 horses working for 1 second.

In the cosmotron, protons are injected tangentially into the main vacuum chamber from a 3.6-Mev Van de Graaff generator. The magnetic field in the cosmotron magnet at injection time is 300 gauss. This must rise to 14,000 gauss when the energy of the protons has increased to 3.1 Bev. The energy gained by the protons for each turn around the cosmotron is approximately 1000 electron volts. An increment of energy is given in 1 pulse every time the protons cross one of the straight sections of the race-track orbit. During the acceleration period, the frequency of the radiofrequency-acceleration voltage must increase so as to synchronize with the particles and the magnetic-field increase. At the time of injection of the protons into the cosmotron, the particles are, of course, relatively slow and the radiofrequency is only 350,000 cycles per second. At the final energy of the 3.1-Bev protons, the frequency of the accelerating pulses has increased to 4.2 million times per second, or a factor of 12 over the initial frequency. This factor of 12 represents an increase in the velocity of the protons by the same ratio; thus one sees (as special relativity predicts and as the designers recognized) that the energy of the protons is no longer proportional to the square of velocity (as it would be in Newtonian mechanics), since in this same acceleration, the energy has increased from 3.6 Mev to 3.1 Bev, or by a factor of approximately 860.

The synchrotron does not produce high-energy particles continuously. Protons must be injected into the orbit in bunches and then brought up to full energy. The control circuits, relating the rise of the guide magnetic field to the accelerating, radiofrequency pulses, take their cue from a beam-pick-up coil in the magnetic field. After suitable analysis of the pick-up signal, the information is fed to an electronic computer that determines and controls the appropriate frequency for the accelerating pulses. In the cosmotron, one burst of particles is handled every 5 seconds. Out of this 5 seconds, approximately 1 second is usefully employed in acceleration, and most of the remaining 4-second *off* period is used in preparing the machine for the next burst. At the end of the acceleration cycle, the high-energy particles can either be extracted into an experimental area or sent crashing against an internal target of solid material that has been *plunged* into the protons' orbit. From such an intensive burst of high-energy particles, a veritable avalanche of lower-energy protons, neutrons, electrons, π mesons, μ mesons, K mesons, hyperons, and gamma rays is unleashed. At one stage in the testing of the performance of the cosmotron, neutrons that were coming from collisions of emergent high-energy protons with nitrogen and oxygen nuclei of the air were detectable several miles *downstream* from the machine. The emergent beam, of course, is now stopped in a 50-foot-thick man-made mountain outside the machine building, and the machine itself is covered by stacked, 12-foot-thick concrete blocks.

Beam-intensity factors
in circular machines

Before the largest existing machines of the early 1960s can be discussed, there is a further and, at first look, minor point about machines that must be raised. This is the question of focusing of the accelerating-proton beam. Focusing is exceedingly important because it controls the intensity of a beam. Since particles cannot, for a variety of reasons, be injected into a machine without having both energy spread and angular spread, there must be some gathering-together force that will retain the particles in the machine. Unless there is some velocity focusing that can bring together those particles, which go either a little faster or a little slower than average, and unless there is some spatial focusing that will deflect back those particles which are diverging slightly compared with those which are exactly on the correct orbit, there will be only very few particles that endure the many millions of revolutions around the track necessary to achieve the final energy. The velocity-focusing property of a synchrotron was first discussed by McMillan and Veksler. It is largely a matter of the right

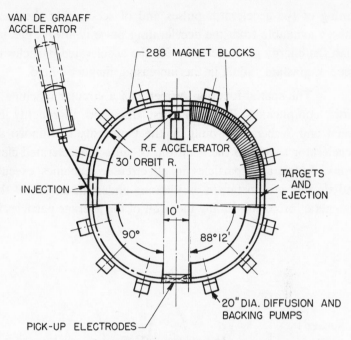

VAN DE GRAAFF ACCELERATOR

288 MAGNET BLOCKS

R.F. ACCELERATOR

30' ORBIT R.

INJECTION

TARGETS AND EJECTION

10'

90°   88°12'

20" DIA. DIFFUSION AND BACKING PUMPS

PICK-UP ELECTRODES

Inside the Cosmotron

The Brookhaven cosmotron, showing the 3-Bev accelerator without the protective, heavy-concrete shielding that surrounds the entire magnet structure when in normal use. One of the quadrant guiding magnets is in the immediate foreground.

At the right, a machine operator is inspecting equipment at one of the straight sections of the vacuum chamber. At this particular straight section, many of the most-important targets are introduced into the beam of accelerated protons. The operator at the left is inspecting one of the 12 large vacuum pumps attached to the ring. The open area in the distance beyond the cosmotron ring itself is the experimental area into which many primary and secondary beams are transported. The technique of handling beams has become a science in its own right. The proton injector which is a Van de Graaff generator, may be seen as a cylindrical tank at the immediate rear of the magnet ring. A schematic diagram of the cosmotron is given above.

timing of the accelerator pulses and of seeing that the peak energy available from the accelerating pulse is always greater than the energy gain necessary for the accelerated particles to keep a constant radius in the increasing magnetic field.

The spatial-focusing property of a circular machine is more complicated. This was first discussed thoroughly by Kerst and Serber, who built (at the University of Illinois) an accelerator known as the betatron, because it accelerated electrons. Accelerated particles in all circular machines execute radial- and axial-betatron oscillations under the action of the magnetic forces controlling the orbit of the average particles in

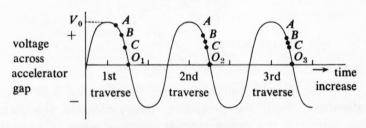

Velocity Focusing

Phase-stable velocity focusing in a proton synchrotron is achieved (1) by changing the magnetic field, in order to keep the particles in the same orbit, (2) by changing the frequency, in order to keep the particles in phase with the accelerating pulses, and (3) by having the peak voltage V_0 greater than that necessary for the particles to keep up with the increasing magnetic field.

Velocity focusing is seen in the particles A, B, and C since they tend to bunch together more and more on later traverses. However, all particles A, B, and C tend to slide toward the $O_{1, 2 \ldots}$ points (where they would receive no impulses), and this tendency is counteracted in the synchrotron by increasing both the magnetic field and frequency of acceleration.

the machine. Owing to the existence of these oscillations and the necessity of keeping the particles circulating, the vacuum vessel of the machine must be larger than the amplitudes of oscillation of the particles. In the cosmotron, the vacuum vessel has a useful aperture 6-inches high and 25-inches wide. In order to accommodate this vacuum chamber, the magnet aperture is approximately 9 by 48 inches; the size of the magnet structure and a large part of the cost of the machine is determined by the size of this aperture. As we have seen, the total weight of the magnet is 2000 tons. Reducing the size of the magnet aperture would reduce the magnet weight and cost, but the consequent reduction in size of the vacuum vessel would lead to a significant loss of intensity in the number of particles accelerated. (We mention parenthetically that the cosmotron accelerates about a million million protons to full energy in a single burst.)

Discovery of strong-focusing principle

Soon after the cosmotron had commenced operation as a research tool, several of the members of the Brookhaven accelerator group began thinking about many features of accelerator design and the best manner of proceeding to higher energies. Based upon the operation of the cosmotron, they were able to develop a radically new method that has revolutionized high-energy-accelerator construction. This new method was the principle of strong focusing, which was worked out by Courant, Livingston, and Snyder at Brookhaven, in 1952.

The background against which the designs of the 30-Bev accelerators at CERN and Brookhaven were developed is of some historic interest. Already in 1949, a quarter-scale model of the Berkeley bevatron operated successfully. This yielded most-valuable information on orbits designed for the Brookhaven cosmotron, which operated at 2 Bev in mid-1952 and at 3 Bev in early 1954. Berkeley's full-scale 6-Bev beva-

tron did not commence operation until 1954. By 1953, designers in Brookhaven were in agreement on an extension, using strong focusing principles, to 20 or 30 Bev. The developments going on in Europe were recently discussed in a review of the first year of operation of the 30-Bev CERN machine. In June 1952, the Interim Council for the European Center for Nuclear Research decided to construct a 10-Bev proton synchrotron, which was to be a scaled-up model of the bevatron. However, on learning, in July 1952, of the new strong-focusing principle proposed by the Brookhaven group, CERN deferred its decision on the 10-Bev accelerator until further studies had been made. In October 1953, both CERN and Brookhaven groups met to discuss and exchange plans; scarcely surprisingly, both had arrived at a design that was to achieve an energy of 30 Bev! Unknown to the Western World, a Russian group during this same period had been going ahead with construction of a 10-Bev accelerator. This accelerator commenced operation during 1957 and was, for about 2 years, the highest-energy machine in the world. However, by defer-

Green, Snyder, and Christofilos

Machine physicists deep in thought during this test of the strong-focusing principle. An electrostatic model was built at the Brookhaven National Laboratory before design of the 30-Bev proton accelerator was completed. Dr. G. K. Green, who was in charge of the high-energy accelerator project, is shown (center) at the controls of the test machine. Dr. H. S. Snyder (left), in the characteristic "thinker" attitude, and Dr. N. Christofilos, seated next to Dr. Snyder, were two of the originators of the strong-focusing principle of acceleration.

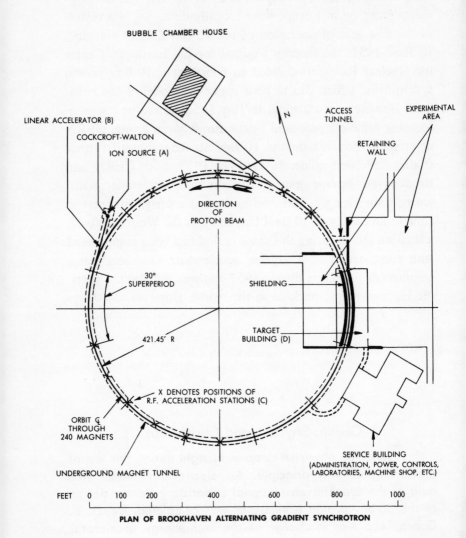

BUBBLE CHAMBER HOUSE

LINEAR ACCELERATOR (B)

COCKCROFT-WALTON

ION SOURCE (A)

ACCESS
TUNNEL

EXPERIMENTAL
AREA

RETAINING
WALL

N

DIRECTION
OF
PROTON BEAM

30°
SUPERPERIOD

SHIELDING

421.45' R

TARGET
BUILDING (D)

X DENOTES POSITIONS OF
R.F. ACCELERATION STATIONS (C)

ORBIT ₵
THROUGH
240 MAGNETS

UNDERGROUND MAGNET TUNNEL

SERVICE BUILDING
(ADMINISTRATION, POWER, CONTROLS,
LABORATORIES, MACHINE SHOP, ETC.)

FEET   0   100   200   400   600   800   1000

PLAN OF BROOKHAVEN ALTERNATING GRADIENT SYNCHROTRON

ring their decision in 1952 and 1953, when the principle of strong focusing was being investigated, the CERN group produced a 30-Bev machine of much-higher intensity than the conventional 10-Bev Russian accelerator, and they did it for practically the same cost. Another interesting sidelight on the history of strong focusing occurred in 1953 when Christofilos, then in the United States, announced that he had already invented this type of focusing several years earlier when he was

Brookhaven A.G.S. Machine
General layout of the Brookhaven A.G.S. machine.

residing in Greece. At a little later date he had transmitted his ideas in a memorandum to the Radiation Laboratory in Berkeley, where his communication had been tucked away, unnoticed, in a filing cabinet for well over a year. Undaunted, Christofilos had proceeded to apply for patent rights on his invention. A logical way out was taken when Christofilos decided to join the Brookhaven Laboratory. Detailed planning for a new accelerator began there in 1953.

In the conventional *weak-focusing* accelerators (as the cosmotron and bevatron are now called), Kerst and Serber showed that radial and axial focusing can be obtained simultaneously only if a certain field-index quantity n lies between zero and unity. The value of n in the Brookhaven cosmotron is 0.6. In the CERN strong-focusing machine, the value of n is 288; thus it cannot simultaneously focus in the radial and axial directions. This large value of n enables the CERN magnets to achieve strong focusing in the axial or vertical direction, but the power of focusing in the radial or horizontal direction is lost. What Courant, Livingston, and Snyder realized was that the radial-focusing property could be recovered by using alternating-magnet sections, which possessed opposite magnetic-field gradients—that is, one section of magnetic field that increased along a radius of the machine toward the center, followed by another section of magnetic field that increased along a radius toward the outer edge of the machine. The strong-focusing principle is, therefore, often referred to as alternating-gradient focusing. The tremendous advantage of strong-focusing operation is the very large reduction in the amplitudes of the betatron oscillations, both axial and radial. We have seen that, whereas the vacuum chamber of the cosmotron has a working aperture of 6 by 25 inches, the CERN and Brookhaven A.G.S. (alternating gradient synchrotron) machines have apertures of only 2¾ by 5½ inches. This results in a large saving of iron for the magnetic-guide field. As Adams, who was director of CERN during the construction of the machine, pointed out, the CERN accelerator has approximately 3 times the energy, 3 times the radius, and 3 times the circumference of the Russian accelerator, yet the CERN magnet is only one-tenth the weight of the Russian magnet. Most of the costs of the convential weak-focusing cosmotron, bevatron, and Russian machines are a result of the magnet. However, although strong focusing in the CERN and Brookhaven machines results in a very economical magnet structure, the desired guide field cannot be obtained without considerable care. One hundred magnet sections in the CERN machine, each 4.3 meters long have to be aligned around a ring of 100-meters radius to a precision of 0.3 millimeter! To preserve such an accuracy of alignment, the temperature of the entire structure has to be maintained constant to 1 degree centigrade. The hundred sections totaling 4000 tons of iron are supported on a single-ring structure of concrete, set in a subterranean tunnel covered with 3 meters of earth.

In operation, the A.G.S. machine at CERN is very similar to a conventional synchrotron. Protons of 50 Mev are injected from a linear accelerator into the vacuum vessel of the accelerator when the guide field is only 120 gauss. As the protons speed up under the action of the accelerating electric pulses, the frequency of the radiofrequency oscillation increases from 3 million to 10 million times per second, and the magnetic guide field increases to 14,000 gauss. The frequency of circulation of the particles is determined by a beam-control monitor, which records the passage of the bunched-proton beam past a fixed point in the orbit. This information is analyzed by an electronic computer that then feeds accelerating pulses of the correct frequency and phase back into the machine. In the CERN machine, it has been found that the beam does not move during the whole acceleration by more than 1 centimeter from the center of the vacuum chamber. At 25 Bev, the number of beam bunches accelerated in the CERN machine is 20 per minute. It is probably not an exaggeration

to describe both the CERN and Brookhaven alternating-gradient synchrotrons as the most accurately functioning, high-energy machines that have thus far been built. Accuracy of design, accuracy of fabrication, and accuracy of assembly have all combined to produce very high intensity beams up to approximately ½ million million protons per pulse at a highly stable energy of approximately 30 Bev.

The accompanying table (page 90) gives the more important high-energy-proton machines that either have been built within the last few years or should soon be completed.

A.G.S. Tunnel

Inside the Brookhaven A.G.S. tunnel, showing a few of the 240 magnet sections.

Proton Synchrotrons (Exceeding 1 Bev) (1962)[a]

Accelerator, type	Energy, Bev	Cost, million dollars	Intensity,[b] protons per pulse	Date of completion
Cosmotron (conv.) (Brookhaven)	3	7	2×10^{11}	1952
Saturne (conv.) (Saclay, France)	3	11	10^{11}	1958
Princeton (conv.)* (Pennsylvania)	3		2×10^{12}	1960
Bevatron (conv.) (Berkeley)	6		2×10^{11}	1954
Nimrod (conv.)* (Harwell, U.K.)	7	17	10^{12}	1962
Dubna (A.G.S.)* (Russia)	7		10^{11}	1960
Dubna (conv.) (Russia)	10		10^{11}	1957
Argonne (Z.G.S.)* (Chicago)	10		2×10^{12}	1962
CERN (A.G.S.) (Geneva)	28	24	2×10^{11}	1959
Brookhaven (A.G.S.) (New York)	30	30	2×10^{11}	1960
Russia (A.G.S.)*	50		10^{11}	1962

[a] Figures given with * were only projected ones when announcements were first made public. In many cases it is seen that the completion date has already passed.

[b] Since modifications have been, and are constantly being, made to improve intensities, many of these figures for normal performance are rather unreliable.

Conv. = conventional synchrotron

A.G.S. = alternating gradient synchrotron

Z.G.S. = zero gradient synchrotron (similar to conventional synchrotron)

The need for special
high-energy-particle detection devices

In 1957, at the end of the Padua-Venice conference, Powell, echoing the feelings of the assembly of physicists said: "Certainly as the energy of the bombarding particle is increased, new technical difficulties arise and much work will have to be done. We shall all follow the fortunes of the new machines with great interest and excitement." With growing interest in higher-and-higher energy particles, new observational techniques have found their way to the forefront of nuclear physics. Let us first look back over the situation in the 1920s and 1930s. The two most widely used instruments of that period were the Geiger counter and the Wilson cloud chamber. Both of these devices are suited to the detection of low-energy particles of a few Mev and having ranges in air of a few centimeters. Care had to be taken to use windows of very low stopping power so that particles could enter the sensitive parts of counter or chamber. It is true that, in the same period, cosmic-ray experiments on very high energy particles were performed with both counter and cloud chamber. Here, however, adaptations were made by interposing absorbing layers of materials between trays of counters and between, or actually in, cloud chambers. These were never entirely satisfactory, though, for phenomena that occurred inside the absorbers could be only partially inferred from observations of the particles that had emerged into the detectors.

Reference has already been made to the advance in high-energy-particle detection using nuclear-photographic techniques. A heavily loaded silver bromide emulsion, which has a density of 4 grams per cubic centimeter, is an efficient stopper of high-energy ionizing particles. Moreover, photographic emulsion is continuously sensitive both in space and time. Very infrequent events, such as those occurring in cos-

Silver Disintegration

A reproduction of a disintegration of a silver nucleus in nuclear photographic emulsion caused by a 28-Bev proton p accelerated in the CERN A.G.S. machine. Coincidentally, the disintegration star has 28 π-meson tracks.

mic rays, can be accumulated by exposures lasting for days. By the late 1950s, emulsion packages of several hundred sheets, each approximately ½ millimeter thick and 1 or 2 feet square were being employed, not only in high-altitude cosmic-ray research, but also in high-energy particle-physics experiments conducted at large machines. In connection with cloud-chamber techniques, the first successful extension was to very large diffusion cloud chambers. Some of the early work, especially around the cosmotron, on π-meson scattering and strange-particle production was done with a 7-foot-long diffusion chamber filled with hydrogen gas at a pressure of 20 atmospheres. The diffusion chamber is a continuously sensitive device in which a condensing rain of alcohol vapor preferentially collects on the charges that are set free by a nuclear particle passing through the chamber gas. In spite of the initial success of the diffusion chamber, another kind of chamber has now almost entirely supplanted it in high-energy nuclear physics.

Development of the bubble chamber

The *bubble* chamber is the 1960 wonder of nuclear physics, just as the Wilson cloud chamber was the miracle of science in the 1920s and 1930s. C. T. R. Wilson is reputed to have commented to a friend in 1955, shortly before he died and just after the bubble chamber had been invented, that he had given some thought to the use of bubbles instead of droplets even as far back as the year 1900. As so often happens, however, nothing is ever invented until it is needed and, back in 1900, a bubble chamber certainly was not needed! That necessity was clearly seen for the first time by Glaser. It is said, probably without any substantiation whatsoever, that the first inspiration for the bubble chamber came while contemplating the bubbles forming in a glass of beer. Although the effect of high-energy nuclear particles on the rate of formation of bubbles in beer is slight, if any, Glaser found that, under the right conditions in certain liquids, bubbles will very definitely form along the track of ionizing nuclear particles. The best conditions for bubble formation are when a liquid is superheated to a temperature well above its boiling point. Glaser found that these conditions could be achieved by heating a liquid under pressure, so that it almost boiled at the increased pressure. When the pressure was suddenly released, the liquid was able to remain for a short time in a superheated state.

If ionizing nuclear particles pass through the liquid just as the pressure is released, bubbles form at *hot spots* produced along the particle tracks. The hot spots are actually made by low-energy, secondary electrons knocked out of atoms by the high-energy particles. Bubbles will also form on the walls of the vessel containing the superheated liquid, but tracks can be seen clearly if they are photographed at the right time, that is, before the wall bubbles have had a chance to grow. (In the later-model bubble chambers, bubble formation on walls and on foreign material in the liquid is prevented by fast recompression of the liquid immediately following photography of the tracks.)

The first bubble chamber, invented by Glaser, was a heavy-walled pyrex-glass bulb, 3-cm long with a 1-cm inside diameter, filled with the organic liquid, diethyl ether. The picture of Glaser's chamber was so completely foreign to the editor of *The Physical Review* that he first printed it upside down! From this small beginning at the University of Michigan, where Glaser first worked on a grant of less than $1000, have grown the behemoths of Berkeley, Brookhaven, and CERN, each costing approximately 2 million dollars. The largest chambers are approximately 72 by 20 by 15 inches and are filled with liquid hydrogen at a temperature of -247 degrees centigrade (26 degrees above the absolute zero!) and operating at a pressure of between 20 and 90 pounds per square inch! As Glaser so aptly remarked: ". . . technical developments . . . have gone the same way as the work of Rutherford, be-

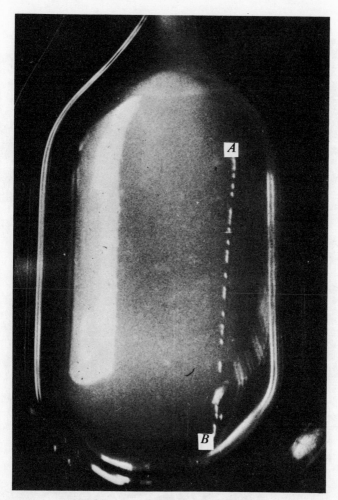

Glaser's Bubble Chamber

Glaser's first bubble chamber—a heavy-walled glass bulb, 3 centimeters long and 1 centimeter inside diameter, filled with diethyl ether. A cosmic-ray-particle track, which was probably a high-energy μ meson, is seen along AB. The curved lines are light reflections from the glass walls of the bulb. The picture was taken with a 20-microsecond-duration flash.

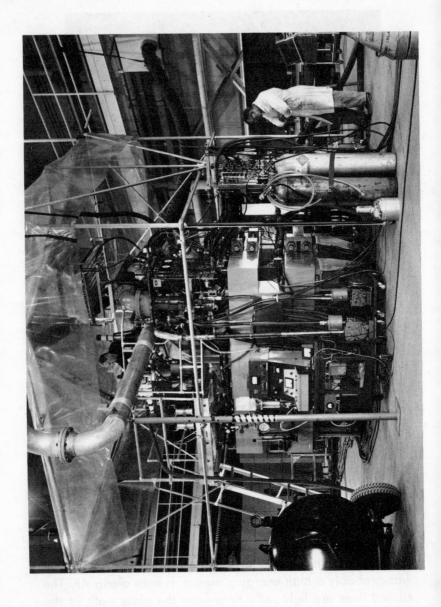

ginning with sealing wax and string and ending up with tons and tons of material."

The great advantages of the liquid-hydrogen bubble chamber are threefold: (1) it has relatively high stopping power, (2) it is homogeneous and provides the most fundamental and simplest target material for interactions with high-energy nuclear projectiles, and (3) it has a large working volume. By virtue of its second characteristic, it outdoes nuclear photographic emulsions, which are a hodgepodge of hydrogen, carbon, nitrogen, oxygen, bromine, and silver. The physicist who uses nuclear emulsions is continually arguing about just which nucleus was struck by the high-energy incident particle. By virtue of its third characteristic, the bubble chamber has eclipsed the diffusion chamber. The bubble-chamber physicist can now follow for many inches, or even feet, the tracks of particles arising from a high-energy interaction. Previously, with the diffusion chamber, the sensitive part of the chamber was often only 2 or 3 inches deep. Many physicists believe that bubble chambers of the future will completely monopolize high-energy nuclear physics. Although other devices, such as solid-scintillation chambers, multiple-counter-telescope arrays, and spark chambers (which we shall not discuss), have certain particular advantages; bubble-chamber devotees argue that only a visual device that is homogeneous and continuous in space and sensitivity is satisfactory for recording the complete interaction of nuclear particles at high energies.

Brookhaven Bubble Chamber

The Brookhaven 20-inch liquid-hydrogen bubble chamber installed in the experimental area of the Brookhaven cosmotron. Two of the bubble-chamber pictures shown in Chapter Two were taken with this apparatus.

Many physicists are now gearing the bubble chamber to high-power analysis equipment, because it is in this aspect of the work that the bubble chamber, or for that matter any visual technique, is limited. Each photograph at present must be *scanned* by proficient observers, and the information in a recognized event must then be transferred to some kind of analysis machine. Let us take a brief look at the magnitude of this job. Suppose that one of the accelerators, like the large synchrotron at CERN, takes 20 pictures per minute, 20 hours per day, for 300 days per year; that is, a total of 7.2 million pictures per year. If it takes a scanner ½ minute to look at a picture and see if it contains any evidence of just *one* feature of particular interest, it will require 40 scanners 300 days, concentrating 5 hours per day, to complete a *single* scanning job. For each picture selected by the scanners for further measurement, the amount of time required by a technical assistant to transfer the information of the picture on to a digital computer may be 2.5 minutes. Assuming that only 1 picture in 10 was selected by the scanners as being useful for the particular problem, the number of assistants required to get this job done in a year is 20. As yet the computer time has not been added, nor has the physicist's time in setting up the problem and analyzing the computer output been accounted for. Confronted with these problems, it is little wonder that attention is being turned, as rapidly as possible, to electronic means of picture scanning and data analysis. There is no doubt that the 1960s will see a vast expansion in this aspect of nuclear-physics technology. Well might Glaser say, "things have got big, they have got out of hand, it has grown to be an engineering problem of enormous proportions . . . it is an unpleasant development, but it seems at the moment inevitable."

four

ACHIEVEMENTS AND THE FUTURE

According to the Stanford University physicist, Panofsky: "We are working in a field where the rate of evolution of new knowledge often exceeds the rate at which parameters of accelerators are extended." Certainly, the gains of high-energy physics from 1940 to 1960, from the purely observational point of view, have been spectacular. The discovery of a whole new class of exotic particles was an exciting surprise. The gains, however, must be reckoned not only in the one field of high-energy physics but in many other branches as well, for there are interconnections, at times direct and at other times more subtle, between different parts of physics.

The τ-θ puzzle

One spectacular case of the interrelationship between high-energy physics and conventional low-energy nuclear physics was seen in 1956 in connection with the tau-theta (τ-θ)

puzzle. Historically, τ and θ particles were, as we have seen, special names assigned to K particles that decayed in different ways. As previously described, the τ meson decays into three π mesons, and the θ meson decays into two π mesons. Every experiment that was performed on these particles indicated that, with the exception of their different modes of decay, they were the same particle. Within the small limits of inaccuracy of measurements, both the τ and θ particles were found to have the same mass and the same lifetime. These facts in themselves may not seem puzzling since many radioactive nuclei are known to decay via different branches. For example, radioactive bismuth of mass 212 (also called thorium C) decays in 64 per cent of the cases by beta decay and 36 per cent by alpha decay. The surprising feature of the τ and θ particles was that, despite the evidence in favor of them being one and the same particle, the nature of their decays pointed to them being entirely different particles. This dilemma was first brought to light by Dalitz, who showed that the τ meson, by decaying into three π mesons, should have had negative parity. On the other hand, the θ meson, by decaying into two pions, must have had positive parity.

The parity concept

A digression is in order here to discuss *parity*, the physicists' meaning of which is very different from the dictionary definition that parity is the quality of being equal or equivalent. Parity was the invention of the Princeton physicist, Wigner, an outstanding mathematical physicist. Because parity has no simple interpretation or counterpart in classical physics it is difficult to explain in nonquantum-mechanical physics terms. To understand parity we have to understand something about quantum or wave mechanics, which describes nuclear particles in terms of wave functions. A wave function of a particle, when squared and multiplied by a small volume of space, describes the chance of finding that particle, for example a τ meson, within the small volume of space considered. The value of the wave function depends on the nature of the particle and on the coordinates specifying the position of the space in which one is trying to find the particle. For these coordinates (relative to some given origin, or center), the wave function will possess a certain definite value. Now the property of parity of a wave function is that, if the position coordinates of the particle are separately changed in sign, a positive-parity wave function will not change its sign, whereas a negative-parity wave function will be found to do so.

A large effort in high-energy physics was directed in the early 1950s toward determining the properties of the π meson, especially the value of its spin and the parity of its wavefunction relative to that of a nucleon. As we have already seen in Chapter Two, the spin of a π meson was found to be zero. Our main interest in this chapter is in discussing the parity of the π meson. Information concerning the parity of the π-meson wavefunction has been obtained by consideration of a number of reactions in which the π meson takes part. We shall briefly touch on only one of these reactions in order to give some impression of the arguments involved in parity determination. A π^- meson, when it has been slowed down to rest, will generally be captured by a positively charged nucleus. If a π^- meson slows down in deuterium, it will be captured by a deuteron (which is a proton and a neutron in close combination) and in most cases will give rise to a reaction in which two neutrons, each of approximately 70 Mev, will be emitted. In this reaction, as in all strong interactions, it has been observed that momentum, energy, spin, angular momentum, charge, parity, etc., are conserved. The argument, therefore goes: If parity is known on the right-hand side (usually the products) of the reaction equation, then the left-hand side (which includes the π meson as one of the initial particles) must have had the same parity. The reasoning is rather involved (and we shall not go through it) in order to reach the conclusion that the two neutrons, arising from the reaction of a slow π meson

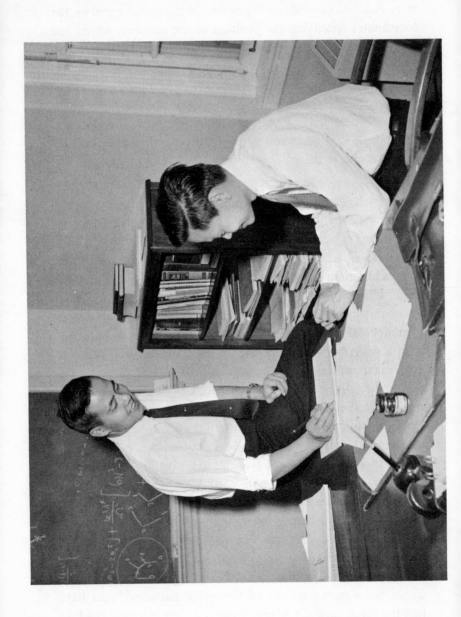

with a deuteron, can only be in a negative parity state. (It is a matter of using Pauli's exclusion principle and arguments of spin and angular momentum). So the conclusion is that, initially, the π meson and the deuteron must have possessed, as a whole, a negative-parity wave function. The final arguments are that (1) the deuteron wave function is known to have positive parity (from very long established nuclear physics), (2) the π meson did not have angular momentum when it was absorbed by the deuteron (and therefore could not have contributed negative parity this way), and (3) the negative parity must have come from the (intrinsic) negative parity of the π meson itself.

Lee and Yang

T. D. Lee and C. N. Yang shortly after being awarded the Nobel Prize in Physics for 1957. In 1956 they put forward the daring proposal that nature did not act symmetrically (in respect to left- and right-handedness) in certain nuclear interactions described as weak.

Physicists were hoping in 1956 to make similar observations on K mesons. However, the K meson, as we have seen, appeared to have either positive or negative parity, depending on the manner of its decay. For scientists to have arrived at this confusing conclusion, the parity of the π-meson wave function had been used as follows: (1) a τ meson decays into three π mésons, each of which has negative parity; it is, therefore, extremely likely (as Dalitz showed from a theoretical analysis of τ-decay observations) that the parity of the τ-meson wave function is also negative; (2) a θ^0 meson may alternatively decay into two identical π^0 mesons; because the π^0 mesons may be interchanged without changing the wave function, the parity of the θ^0-meson wave function must be positive. If the τ and θ were one and the same particle, no such duplicity had ever been heard of before! Since the early 1930s, when the notion of parity had been introduced, states of opposite parity had not been known to mix. For over 20 years, until τ and θ decays were observed, every nuclear process had appeared to be in accord with the principle of the conservation of parity.

Solution of the τ-θ puzzle

In 1956, two brilliant young physicists, Yang and Lee, at this time working together at the Brookhaven National Laboratory, decided to look more closely into the validity of the principle of parity conservation. They concluded that the experimental evidence was in favor of parity conservation in strong, or fast, reactions, such as the disintegration of a nucleus by energetic protons. In weak, or slow, reactions, such as the relatively slow beta decay of a nucleus and the decay of some of the new elementary particles, Yang and Lee decided that the principle of parity had not, until then, been sufficiently and accurately tested. They made a theoretical investigation of the consequences to be expected from a breakdown of the principle, and they suggested a number of decisive experiments that would put the principle to test.

One of the tests they suggested be made was on the decay of a π meson into a μ, followed by the decay of the μ meson into an electron (π-μ-e decay). If parity was not conserved, they predicted that the probability would not be the same (1) for the emission of an electron in the direction of emission of its parent μ as (2) for the emission of an electron in the direction opposite to its parent μ. As it turned out, Yang and Lee were right; the numbers of electrons in the two directions were not equal, and parity was indeed *not* conserved. Experimentally, when the number of positive electrons coming from positive μ mesons were measured, it was found that significantly more, to the extent of 20 to 30 per cent more, positive electrons were emitted backward than forward to the μ-meson's motion. Parity is not conserved in π-μ decay either; since this decay is a two-body system in outgoing particles and is somewhat easier to study than μ-e decay (although harder to experiment with), it will now be more fully discussed.

When a μ meson is emitted from a π-meson decay, we have seen that a neutrino goes off in a direction opposite to the μ meson. Both the μ meson and the neutrino have spin, and, since the π meson has no spin, we have also observed that the μ meson and neutrino must spin in opposite directions in order to conserve spin. This is illustrated in diagram (*a*) on page 106, where, for sound theoretical reasons, we have drawn the spin axes of the particles, and especially of the neutrino, along the lines of motion of the particles. As a matter of fact, we have drawn the neutrino spin opposite, that is, in the sense of a left-hand screw, to its motion. These anticipations are fully justified by experimental evidence.

The question now arises: How can a test of conservation of parity in the π-μ decay be made? One answer is, observe the π-μ decay in a mirror! By "in a mirror," we mean the ex-

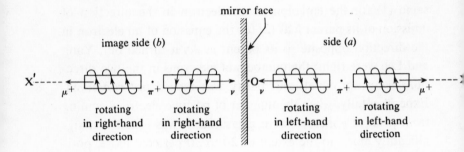

image side (b)   mirror face   side (a)

X' μ^+ π^+ ν O ν π^+ μ^+

rotating in right-hand direction   rotating in right-hand direction   rotating in left-hand direction   rotating in left-hand direction

Nonconservation of Parity

Diagram (a) represents the decay of a π^+ meson as it has been experimentally shown to occur. A μ^+ meson and a neutrino ν are sent out in opposite directions, both spinning in the directions of left-hand screws advancing in the directions of the particles. Diagram (b) is the exact mirror image of (a) in the plane-surface mirror placed at an origin O. Diagram (b), however, is not identical with diagram (a) because in (b) the particles are spinning, not as left-hand screws, but rather as right-hand screws.

If π decays were a 50 per cent mixture of decays looking like type (a) and 50 per cent looking like type (b), we should not be able to tell the difference experimentally between the real thing and its mirror image, and we would say that parity was conserved. (It must be remembered that all experiments in quantum and nuclear phenomena are made only on a statistical basis of a large number of events.) We find, however, that only π^+ decays of type (a) occur, and we can actually observe the difference between the real decays and their mirror image—we say, therefore, that parity is not conserved.

perimenter must not merely look at a reflection of the experiment, but rather that he must try to visualize how the experiment would look if he and the whole experiment were in the imaginary space "on the other side of the mirror." If parity is conserved, the mirror experiment will look exactly like the actual experiment; if the mirrored and actual experiments are not identical, parity is not conserved. In fact, conservation of parity is simply the formal consequence of the postulate that all experiments must be unchanged, i.e., *invariant* under mirroring. The mirror is appropriate because mirror reflection is a way of changing the sign of particle coordinates; this change of sign, as we have seen, is the operation whose effect on the wave function determines the parity.

To test the π-μ decay, therefore in (a) of the figure on page 106 we show a diagram of the π-μ decay as it actually takes place; in (b) of the same diagram is illustrated the reflection of the decay in the mirror at O (note that coordinates along OX′ are the negative of the corresponding coordinates along OX). In the actual experiment (a), an observer at the point labeled π^+ (where the π meson was located when it decayed) would see an outgoing neutrino spinning counterclockwise, or in the direction a screwdriver would be turned as it advanced a left-handed screw along the neutrino path. Now, if an observer stands in front of a mirror and rotates his finger in a counterclockwise direction, he will see the end of his reflected finger also rotating in a counterclockwise direction. In other words, the observer at π^+ on the real side (a) of the mirror sees in the mirror an *approaching* counterclockwise rotating neutrino. The observer *inside* the mirror, however, at π^+ on the image side (b), sees an outgoing clockwise rotating neutrino, because a clockwise rotation viewed from one side looks counterclockwise when viewed from the other side. Whereas the real observer says that, in π-μ decay, the outgoing neutrino (seen from the point where the decay occurred) rotates counterclockwise, the observer inside the mirror (looking at the corresponding mirrored decay) says the outgoing neutrino is rotating clockwise. We conclude that the π-μ decay does not look exactly alike to the real and mirrored observers, whence follows the further conclusion that parity is not conserved in π-μ decay.

Concept of predictability
within quantum-mechanical theory

We must definitely bear in mind, however, that the whole argument of the above paragraph depended on the presumption that *every* time a π^+ meson decays, it emits a left-handed neutrino. If π^+ mesons sometimes emitted left-handed neutrinos and sometimes emitted right-handed neutrinos (if the probabilities of emitting clockwise or counterclockwise neutrinos were equal on the average), parity would have been conserved. Let us elaborate this assertion, which goes to the heart of what is meant by *invariance under mirroring*. Suppose that any one π^+ meson emits either a left-hand or right-hand neutrino, which becomes, respectively, a right- or left-hand neutrino on mirroring, as we have explained. If two kinds of neutrinos can be emitted, then what any one π^+ meson does is not significant. In fact, according to quantum mechanics, if there are two alternative types of decay, then what any one π^+ meson will do is quite unpredictable. What is predictable is the average result of a large number of decays, and an experiment consists of observing this large number; observing a single π^+ decay is not a meaningful experiment in the quantum-mechanical sense. If a large number of π-μ decays are observed, in which on the average 50 per cent emit right-handed neutrinos and 50 per cent emit left-handed neutrinos, then obviously the mirrored experimenter will also observe, on the average, equal numbers of right-handed and left-handed neutrinos; in this circumstance, therefore, one would conclude parity is conserved, as has been asserted earlier in this paragraph.

As it happens, however, the π^+ meson does not have

two alternatives. Every time it decays, the outgoing neutrino is left-handed as in (a). Demonstrating this fact experimentally is far from easy; in fact, it has been accomplished only recently (1960 and 1961). Correspondingly, the emitted μ^+ meson always rotates in the left-hand direction compared to its direction of motion. (It is actually experimentally easier to measure the spinning direction of μ^- than μ^+. Three groups of workers, at Dubna, U.S.S.R., at CERN, and at Columbia University have each recently demonstrated that the helicity of the μ^- is positive; that is, the negative μ meson spins as a right-handed screw. The logical inference is that the μ^+ has negative helicity.) Historically, nonconservation of parity was earlier shown to occur for μ-meson decay into an electron and two neutrinos. Although a discussion of the μ decay will

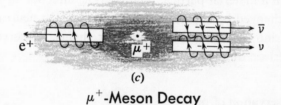

(c)

μ^+-Meson Decay

A μ^+ meson has just decayed spontaneously into a positron e^+ and two neutrinos. A neutrino ν and an antineutrino $\bar{\nu}$ in this picture have been emitted along the same line, in a direction opposite to the positive electron e^+. This will lead to the e^+ having the maximum possible energy. The two neutrinos, however, need not have the same momenta or the same directions of emission.

Since spin is conserved in the event shown, the direction of spin of the electron is along the same direction as the μ meson was spinning before decay. Based on the discovery in 1962 of two types of neutrinos, it is probable that the ν is one type associated only with electrons (in this case, e^+), and $\bar{\nu}$ is another type associated only with μ mesons.

not be entered into, analysis has shown that the decay is consistent with a diagram such as that on page 109.

It is a fascinating sidelight on both man and nature to recall a comment by Pauli on nonconservation of parity at the time experiments first demonstrated the correctness of the Yang and Lee predictions. Pauli's comment was that he "couldn't believe God was a weak left-hander." By this he meant he could not believe that, when neutrinos are created, they rotate in the direction of a left-hand screw (when one looks in the direction and sense of their motion). As a matter of fact, Pauli already knew, some years before 1956, that parity could not be conserved in beta decay if the neutrino had just this property. At that time he flatly rejected such a theory of neutrinos and beta decay for just the reason that it did not allow parity to be conserved! It will be noticed in diagram (c) that the neutrino v rotates in a left-hand way, but the antineutrino $\bar{v}$ rotates in a right-hand direction. Whereas the direction of spin of a material particle relative to its direction of motion can be changed by experimental techniques, the neutrino and antineutrino, once launched on their flights, preserve their characteristic directions of spin.

Nonconservation of parity in beta decay

Probably the greatest impact of the discovery of the nonconservation of parity in weak interactions was felt by low-energy physicists working in the field of beta decay. In fact, the first experimental test of the breakdown of parity conservation was demonstrated by the beta decay of the cobalt nucleus Co^{60}. Yang and Lee predicted, if parity was not conserved, that beta decay would not be symmetrical in space with respect to the direction of spin of the parent radioactive nucleus. In order to perform this experiment, Wu, of Columbia University, and a group of low-temperature physicists at the National Bureau of Standards, Washington, D.C., had first to set up or

polarize the direction of spin of the radioactive Co⁶⁰ nuclei.
This was done by adding small amounts of radioactive Co⁶⁰ to
single crystals of cerium magnesium nitrate and then cooling
the crystals to a temperature of lower than −272 degrees
Centigrade. This temperature, incidentally, is only 1 degree
above the absolutely lowest temperature obtainable. When
cooled in this fashion, the Co nuclei will preferentially set
themselves in the direction of an externally applied magnetic

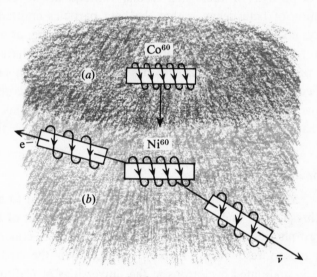

Cobalt Decay

The radioactive nucleus Co⁶⁰ is here depicted as decaying into Ni⁶⁰ with the emission of a beta particle e⁻ and
an antineutrino $\bar{v}$. The direction of emission of the beta particle is not symmetrical with respect to the direction of spin
of the Co⁶⁰ nucleus. There is a much higher probability for
the beta particle to be emitted opposite to the direction of
the Co⁶⁰ spin. Two units of spin are taken off by the beta
particle and antineutrino together, and these units represent
the difference of 10 units of spin for the original Co⁶⁰ nucleus
and 8 units of spin remaining on the Ni⁶⁰ nucleus after the
disintegration.

field. All this was a difficult experiment that could only have been done by close collaboration between many physicists working in different, highly specialized branches of physics. The upshot of the experiment was that the electrons were found to be emitted mainly backward from aligned Co^{60} nuclei, in the manner illustrated by the figure on page 111. It can be seen that "mainly backward" in the actual experiment implies mainly forward in the mirrored experiment. That is, it demonstrates (as Yang and Lee pointed out) nonconservation of parity. An interesting further consequence of this description of beta decay is that the beta particles emitted are always polarized, that is, their spins are always along, or opposite to, their directions of motion at emission. This characteristic property of beta particles has subsequently been amply verified, and a very much deeper insight into the theoretical nature of beta decay has resulted from investigations that started in the apparently unrelated field of strange particles.

Resonance interactions

Another group of experiments that we appear to be on the threshold of understanding and that has come out of high-energy physics in the 1950s and early 1960s, is concerned with meson resonances. Back in 1950, when the first frequency-modulated cyclotrons at the universities of California, Chicago, and Columbia had just started to produce intense beams of π mesons, experiments using hydrogen showed that beams of π mesons were strongly scattered by protons. This strong scattering is one of the most direct ways of demonstrating that there are strong interactions between π mesons and protons. Unfortunately, but, it seems, inevitably in the high-energy-physics field, these cyclotrons were not able to produce sufficiently high energy π mesons for a full investigation of the problem. It was left for the workers using the cosmotron at Brookhaven in 1952 and 1953 to show that a very strong resonance peak occurs at approximately 160 Mev in the scattering of both π^- and π^+ mesons by protons. The fundamental nature of this peak is still being discussed, but there is a strong indication that a meson and a nucleon may exist in an excited short-lived state that probably should be regarded as having an independent existence. It is true that this excited state does not exist for more than about 10^{-23} seconds, but the borderline between real and potentially real states is indeed very broad, if not continuous.

Other resonance peaks appearing in the scattering of π mesons by nucleons have also been observed at higher π-meson energies. The same resonances can also be excited by

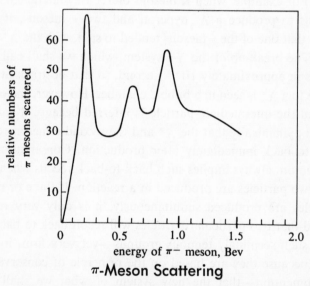

π-Meson Scattering

When beams of π mesons are scattered by protons, the number of mesons scattered is found to change with the energy of the π meson. The curve of this figure shows the energy variation of the relative numbers of π^- mesons scattered by protons. Up to an energy of 1.5-Bev π^- energy in the laboratory, three *resonance-scattering* peaks are evident. These peaks are believed to be associated with resonance particles formed momentarily from π mesons and nucleons.

other means, such as by irradiating with high-energy γ rays and by direct, high-energy collisions between nucleons themselves. This again tends to support the idea of independent-particle existence.

Resonance particles

Another wave of excitement among high-energy physicists broke out in mid-1960 when experiments with high-energy K particles led to the discovery of meson resonances with other particles, such as hyperons and K mesons, themselves. The evidence for the independence of these new resonance states is based mainly on a number of production reactions. For example, when K mesons of 1.1 Bev interacted with protons to produce a Λ^0 hyperon and two π mesons, it was found that one of the π mesons tended to stick with the Λ^0 particle. The break-up of the Λ-π system, which we shall call Λ^*, occurs in approximately 10^{-23} second, so that no track attributable to a Λ^* is seen in a bubble chamber. However, the existence of the intermediate particle is inferred because it can be shown dynamically that the Λ^* and the second π meson recoil back to back immediately after production. Conservation of momentum always implies such back-to-back recoils whenever only two particles are produced in a reaction. If three or more particles are produced simultaneously, it is only very rarely indeed that two particular particles will recoil back to back. It is on such seemingly tenuous grounds—yet very firm, in this case, because they are based on the principle of conservation of momentum—that the new system of what we shall call *resonance particles* has been identified. These short-lived fundamental particles are the ones we hinted at in Chapter Two when the long-lived fundamental particles were being discussed (see the table on page 30). As of 1962, some of the known resonance particles, the nature of which is yet subject to a great deal of conjecture, are given in the accompanying table (page 115).

Resonance Particles (1962)

Particle state	Particle mass, Mev
η (eta) (3π)	550
ρ (rho) (2π)	760
ω (omega) (3π)	790
K^* (K-π)	880
N_1^* (p-π)	1237
Λ^* (Λ-π)	1384
Y^* (Λ-2π or Σ-π)	1405
N_2^* (p-π)	1516
N_3^* (p-π)	1683

Direct interactions
using high-energy neutrinos

The first experiment using high-energy neutrinos was completed in mid-1962. The magnitude of this experiment was far beyond any one single previous experiment in high-energy physics. It was commenced at the Brookhaven A.G.S. machine in October 1961, and, before a halt was called in June 1962, 800 hours of prime machine time had been used. For normal, high-energy-physics experiments, most researchers are only too-well aware of the problems of obtaining even 8 hours of machine time. This first neutrino experiment involving a high-energy machine cost more than 1 million dollars, and 7 top-flight physicists from Columbia University teamed up in order to make an all-out attack on the problem. This was only a small part of the effort, for the experiment had strong support of the theoretical team on weak interactions—Yang, Lee, and Feinberg—and was fully supported by technical groups at Brookhaven National Laboratory and Columbia University.

The aim of the experiment was to determine whether neutrinos, obtained from the decay of μ mesons, could produce both of the so-called inverse-beta-decay processes of the nucleon. In actual fact, four possible inverse processes have to be considered. This is because both neutrinos and antineutrinos are produced from the decays of charged mesons. As we have already seen in Chapter Two, these decay processes are

$$\pi^+ \rightarrow \mu^+ + \nu \quad \text{and} \quad \pi^- \rightarrow \mu^- + \bar{\nu}$$

Ordinary neutrinos ν are considered associated with μ^+, or antiparticle μ mesons; antineutrinos $\bar{\nu}$ are associated with μ^-, or ordinary μ mesons. (These associations follow from consideration of the principle of conservation of leptons. The number of leptons on one side of an equation equals the sum of the real leptons and the antileptons.) The four inverse reactions that must be considered are

$$\nu + n \rightarrow p + e^- \quad \text{and} \quad \bar{\nu} + p \rightarrow n + e^+$$

producing electrons, and

$$\nu + n \rightarrow p + \mu^- \quad \text{and} \quad \bar{\nu} + p \rightarrow n + \mu^+$$

producing μ mesons.

From what has been mentioned in Chapter Two, it will be recalled that Cowan and Reines in 1956 had already observed the inverse beta reaction that produced electrons. In that experiment they used low-energy neutrinos emitted from beta decays taking place in a nuclear reactor (or uranium pile). These neutrinos had energies generally less than 10 Mev and were unable to bring about the production of μ mesons, which requires energies greater than at least 107 Mev (since the mass of the μ meson, which has to be created out of energy, is 107 Mev).

From the results of the high-energy-neutrino experiments, however, it appears certain that, even though the Cowan and Reines experiments had used neutrinos of many hundreds of Mev, they would still not have produced μ mesons. The reason is that the latest experiments show there are two types of neutrinos—those associated with electrons in beta decay, and others associated with μ mesons in π- and K-meson decays. The μ-meson decay, into an electron and two neutrinos, presumably has one type of neutrino from the μ-meson part of the process and the other type of neutrino from the electron part of the process. This curious association of two types of neutrinos must be the explanation of why the μ meson has not been observed to decay sometimes into an electron and a γ ray (photon). In fact, it is a happy way out of the dilemma that theoretical physicists were in when they calculated that a μ meson should have decayed into an electron and a photon once in about 10,000 times of the normal decay, if ν and $\bar{\nu}$ from the μ decay were true particle and antiparticle of one another.

Neutrino experiments at Brookhaven

The A.G.S.-neutrino experiments were performed with an intense high-energy-neutrino *beam* produced in a very novel way. Every 1.2 seconds, a pulse of about 3×10^{11} protons was accelerated up to an energy of 15 Bev in the A.G.S. machine. At the end of the acceleration cycle, the proton bunch was made to strike a beryllium-metal target suddenly plunged into the protons' orbit. An intense spray of secondary particles, mainly π mesons but also containing some 10 per cent of K mesons and hyperons, was thus produced from the target. The mesons, of a wide range of energies, were allowed to proceed out from the target for about 70 feet where they then plowed into a 36-foot-thick wall of solid iron. The purpose of the iron was to stop the mesons completely and the purpose of the 70-foot flight path was to allow some of the π mesons to decay into μ mesons and neutrinos before the iron wall was reached. Approximately 10 per cent of the π mesons decayed into neutrinos that then were able to proceed in the same forward direction and form the neutrino beam. The 36-foot wall of iron was needed much less to stop the π mesons than the μ mesons, which were produced alongside the neutrinos in the π decay. As we have seen, μ mesons do not interact strongly with matter, and the only way they can be taken out of the neutrino beam is to fritter away their energy by letting them ionize atoms—a relatively slow process. However, the iron shield was thick enough to stop μ mesons of energies as high as 17 Bev. This is the reason that the A.G.S. machine was run only at 15 Bev, although, as we have seen in Chapter Three, the machine is capable of producing protons of energies up to 33 Bev. As far as the neutrinos were concerned, the shield was quite insignificant; in fact, the shield

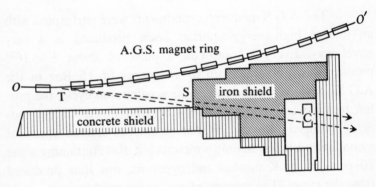

High-Energy-Neutrino Experiments

Lay-out at the Brookhaven A.G.S. machine for the first high-energy-neutrino experiments (1962). An accelerated beam of 15-Bev protons struck a beryllium target at *T*, and a spray of secondary particles was sent in the direction of a 10-ton spark chamber located at *C*. From *T* to *S*, a distance of 69 feet, 10 per cent of secondary π mesons decayed to neutrinos. From *S* to *C*, through 45 feet of iron shielding, all π and μ mesons from the secondary beam were filtered out. An essentially pure neutrino beam penetrated through to the spark chamber *C*, in which a very few neutrino interactions were observed.

would have had to be as thick as the diameter of the sun (865,000 miles) in order to have stopped one-half the neutrinos issuing from the A.G.S. target!

In the middle of a small room lined with 20-foot-thick concrete walls and situated immediately behind the 36-foot iron shield, the Columbia University experimenters operated a huge spark chamber. Huge is not an absolute term, and like records is a description made to be broken. However, the spark chamber used was at least 10 times larger than any other until 1962. It was built from 90 plates of aluminum metal, approximately 4-feet square and 1-inch thick. The plates were spaced ½ inch apart by electric-insulating separators, and a voltage was connected to the plates so that sparks occurred between them when a charged particle, causing ionization, broke down the gas insulation between the plates. Such spark chambers are the newest devices in high-energy physics. They have certain advantages over bubble chambers, including simplicity, cheapness, the fact that they can be synchronized to machine pulses, and the ease with which they can be constructed to almost any size desired. The chamber used by the Columbia group had 10 tons of aluminum plates. The same group is now planning to build a chamber of 50 tons, and another group working on neutrino experiments at CERN is developing a chamber of 30 tons.

We shall not enter here into the details of the operation of the spark chamber (for example, how it was timed to operate only when the A.G.S. machine delivered a neutrino beam). Nor shall we discuss the manner in which the chamber was shielded against a background of cosmic-ray μ mesons, which could have been confused with the ones that came from neutrino interactions with protons and neutrons in the aluminum nuclei of the spark chamber. It turned out that in 800 hours of machine-operating time, in which approximately one-third of a billion billion protons hit the target, that 51 true events were observed. Elaborate checks were carried out to be sure that the events were real-inverse-neutrino reactions. The 51 events were characterized as:

(1) 29 *elastic* events in which only one track, a μ meson, was observed. These events were all consistent with either

$$\nu + \text{n} \rightarrow \text{p} + \mu^- \quad \text{or} \quad \bar{\nu} + \text{p} \rightarrow \text{n} + \mu^+$$

and none was consistent with the production of an electron track;

(2) 22 *inelastic* events in which there was more than one track, one of which, however, was always a μ meson. In these events the associated track or tracks could be caused by π mesons, electrons, or γ rays.

The important conclusion was that a μ meson was always produced by the interaction of a neutrino arising from π-meson decay (and therefore initially arising with a μ meson). A direct-elastic event producing an electron was never observed. Their experiments therefore pointed unequivocally to the existence of two types of neutrinos that play similar roles in association with electrons and μ mesons but that do not mix their associations. We therefore see that the number of different particles continues to grow, and theorists are now confidently suggesting, on the basis of the outcome of the neutrino experiments, that another particle, the W particle, also exists. This is an intermediate particle that may take part in weak decays, such as that of the neutron, the π meson, and other particles. New experiments using more-intense and higher-energy neutrinos are now underway, and these may throw further light on the nature of the weak interactions.

Electric and magnetic structure of the nucleon

Another important investigation, which has been made possible by high-energy physics, is an elucidation of the electric and magnetic structure of the proton and neutron. The diameter of a nucleon is known to be on the order of 0.1 of a million millionth (10^{-13}) of a centimeter; in order to investigate parts of the charge distribution within these small dimensions, it is necessary to have a probe whose size is as small as the nucleon itself. Just as physicists, chemists, and biologists turned to electron microscopes in order to see smaller objects than are visible with the ordinary optical microscope, physicists investigating nucleon structures have now used electrons of the highest-available energies. The group at Stanford University, headed by the 1961 Nobel Laureate, Hofstadter, who initiated this work on nuclear structure, has used a linear accelerator to obtain electrons of 1 Bev. Another group at Cornell University has employed electrons from a 1.3-Bev synchrotron. An electron of 1 Bev has a wavelength slightly less than the radius of a proton. From classical optics, it is well known that the smallest points in a microscope image that one may see resolved from one another are only as small as the wavelength of light used. Electrons are also particularly useful for probing the charge structure of the nucleon because they are not subject to specific nuclear forces, other than those of an electric and magnetic nature. The measurements consist of measuring precisely the intensity of electrons scattered by protons at large angles to an incident electron beam. Results immediately show that the charge of a proton is spread, non-uniformly in radius (but presumably symmetrically in angle), over a small but finite spherical volume, the radius of which is on the order of 10^{-13} centimeters. Similar experiments have also been performed on the heavy isotope of hydrogen whose nucleus contains one proton and one neutron. From the difference of the two experiments, the charge distribution in the neutron can be also derived. Both Stanford and Cornell university groups agree on the broad outlines of the structure of the proton and neutron. They may be described as follows:

The charge of the nucleon can be considered in three parts: (1) A *core* part of positive charge for both the neutron

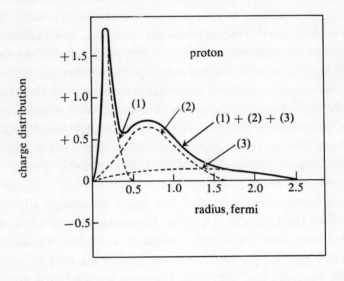

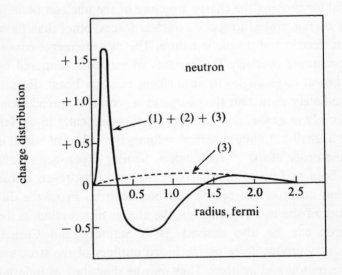

and proton. The fraction of the proton's charge in this part, which extends to about 4×10^{-14} centimeter, is approximately 0.4. (2) A so-called *vector* part, which is positive for the proton and negative for the neutron, accounts for approximately 0.5 of the proton's charge. This part is supposed to be associated with a *virtual* π meson in the nucleon. (3) A so-called *scalar* part, consisting of an outer long tail, which is the same for both the proton and the neutron. The fraction of charge in this part is approximately 0.1 of the total proton charge. How to reconcile these complicated structures of the neutron and proton with the fact that they are regarded as *elementary* particles is a very important problem today.

Charge Distributions

Distributions of charge in proton and neutron are given as functions of the radius within the particle. Three regions of charge may be distinguished in both proton and neutron: (1) core, (2) vector charge, and (3) scalar charge. The area under the proton curve (1) + (2) + (3) is equal to the total proton charge. The area under the neutron curve, (1) + (2) + (3) is equal to zero. (A fermi is a unit of length, equal to 10^{-13} centimeter, commonly used by high-energy physicists. By international agreement in 1961, however, the fermi was discarded in favor of fentometer, which means in Scandinavian, fifteen, i.e., 10^{-15} meter.)

Some future problems

What can be said of the future? The most appropriate predictions are probably extensions of the present. And the important, main-stream problems of the present day are probably the ones we have already discussed. In high-energy physics, they are, briefly: the problem of new particles, the problem of neutrinos and weakly interacting particles, the problem of interparticle resonances, and the problem of nucleon structure. Relative to all these projects, physicists generally agree that they will need higher-energy particles and higher-intensity beams than present machines provide. Let us consider, quite briefly indeed, each of these problems.

New particles? No one in 1942 predicted the existence of strange particles; neither would anyone predict in 1962 that other types of new particles do not exist. Certainly, most physicists will admit, higher energies are most likely to produce new particles. However, the energies that are important in any production process are those that are actually available in the so-called center-of-mass system of the producing particles themselves.

We should realize that the energy available for conversion into the mass of created particles is generally less than the energy of the projectile particle in the laboratory (i.e., with respect to the fixed-measuring instruments in the laboratory system). This is because the projectile and target particles must continue to move through the laboratory after the collision with velocities such that the combined momenta of the particles exactly equal the momentum of the projectile particle before collision. This is the principle of conservation of momentum, which has never been observed to fail. The only energy that is available for the creation of particles is the energy in the center-of-mass system. The center of mass is so defined that the total momentum of the particles relative to this point is always zero. The largest amount of energy that is available for the production of new particles occurs when the colliding particles stick together after the collision. The two particles then move along with a velocity that imparts to them, together, the same momentum as the projectile had just before it collided. For a stationary-target particle, the energy available for production of new particles increases only slowly as the laboratory energy of the projectile particle is increased. For instance, in order to produce a proton-antiproton pair by means of a high-energy proton colliding with another stationary proton, we have seen in Chapter One that Chamberlain and Segrè required a 6-Bev proton from the bevatron. If, however, two protons could have been made to approach one another with equal speeds and collide head-on, it would have been possible to have produced a proton-antiproton pair with only two, 1-Bev protons. This is the reason that many physicists are excited by the possibility of using *clashing* beams of particles to produce new particle varieties. A group of accelerator physicists in the United States (Midwest University Research Association—MURA) has designed a high-energy machine that, energetically, could produce many particle-antiparticle pairs from collisions of oppositely moving particles.

Neutrinos? Now that the first high-energy-neutrino experiments have been performed and it has been found that there are two types of neutrinos, the question being asked is: Why are there two sets of neutrinos?—just as questions had already been asked concerning why there are two sets of charged leptons like the electron and μ meson, which apparently have very similar characteristics and yet differ so widely in mass. Theoretical physicists are, of course, interested in the whole question of weak interactions. They have raised the question: Why should the weak-beta-decay interaction involve four particles? The four particles are: the particle that decays, the particle that is left, the charged lepton (an electron or a μ meson), and an uncharged lepton (a neutrino), for instance,

$n \rightarrow p + e^- + \bar{\nu}$. Many theoreticians would be happier with two 3-particle interactions, such as would occur if an intermediate particle were involved. The decay particle would first decay into the intermediate particle and the final particle, and the intermediate particle would then (perhaps in an extremely short time) break up into a lepton and a neutrino. Yang and Lee have called one such form of the intermediate particle, a W particle, implying that it takes part in weak interactions. They have made a study of the properties such a W particle might be expected to have. The next round in the high-energy-neutrino investigations is to search for evidence of the W particle.

On the experimental side of the neutrino problem, it is certain that more demands will be made for higher and higher neutrino intensities. This is likely to become a more-critical problem as pressure for more machine time increases at the A.G.S. centers. Already, plans at CERN and Brookhaven are well along for improving neutrino beams. The next modification is to extract the proton beams from the machines, so that the secondary-π-meson beams (which furnish the neutrinos by decay) can be taken in the same direct-forward direction as the protons. (In the present systems this cannot be done, since the protons are circulating around the machine ring, and it is not practical because of the structure of the ring to obtain a completely forward beam.) This modification should lead to a considerable increase in intensity. Another suggestion is to use a magnetic horn in order to concentrate the π mesons from the target into a forward cone, instead of, at present, allowing the π mesons to merely spray out from the target. It would now seem assured that any plans for future accelerators must take into account provision for intense neutrino beams.

More resonances? Yes there will undoubtedly be much more information added to our present knowledge on inter-particle resonances. In many ways, this topic is currently the most exciting in the field of high-energy nuclear physics. It is at a stage of development similar in interest to that felt during the breakthrough on parity violation in 1956. There is, at present, a feeling among many physicists that the new short-lived states hold a clue to the understanding of the inner reaches of elementary particles, particularly the nucleons themselves. A large amount of information on the resonant states will be accumulated from the existing machines. As we have already seen in this chapter, experimental information is very rapidly being gathered.

The experimental requirements for higher capabilities in this direction are probably both higher-intensity beams from accelerators and faster methods of analyzing bubble-chamber information. More beam intensity requires either higher-intensity machines and increased available experimental areas around machines, or more duplication of machines currently operating. Considerable discussion of these possibilities is now taking place, and a number of high-intensity machines are now under construction.

Nucleon and other particle structures? In many ways these problems are bound up with the earlier ones of elementary particles and resonant states. In fact, one of the direct-theoretical outgrowths of Hofstadter's work on the structure of the neutron and proton, discussed earlier in this chapter, was the prediction of new elementary particles that would help to properly understand the observed structures. Before the so-called ω- and ρ-resonant particles were observed in the production processes that we have encountered in this chapter, a number of particles with properties like these states had been predicted. This is one of the many instances of the close relationship existing between present-day theoretical and experimental physicists.

It is too early to say what part the new excited- or resonant-state particles play in the structure of fundamental particles. At this time (1962) there are two theoretical schools of thought on this question. One theoretical group is inclined to regard the new short-lived resonant states as purely elementary particles, which are related to separate types of interactions and their particular *fields* of origin. Another theoretical group tends to regard them in the more experimental light of resonant states, which are involved in the scattering interactions of the particles.

The problem of future machines

It may be claimed without fear of much contradiction that higher-energy beams of particles, especially of electrons, will be required in order to study particle structures in greater detail in the future. Higher-intensity machines are also necessary for this problem, too, since large-angle scatterings, from which the more probing information is obtained, are infrequent events.

In October 1961, it was announced that the U.S. Congress had released funds for construction of a 20-Bev-electron accelerator to be built at Stanford University. This accelerator is to be a 2-mile-long traveling-wave linear accelerator. We did not described this type of accelerator in Chapter Three, although it has been mentioned by name, and it forms the injector of protons for the Brookhaven and CERN alternating-gradient machines. The particular advantage of this type of accelerator—and it is this which makes it really the only suitable type of accelerator for electrons of more than approximately 10 Bev—is that it accelerates charged particles with negligible radiation losses of energy. (Circular machines have losses of electromagnetic radiation from particles because of their continually changing directions of motion in the circular orbits.) The Stanford accelerator will be powered by high-frequency radiowaves traveling along the 2-mile evacuated pipe and carrying with them bunches of electrons in much the same way as a surfer rides a wave. Ultimately, the machine is designed to accelerate 60 microamperes of electron current up to

45 Bev. It will have, by far, the highest-average-output power of any machine. The Brookhaven A.G.S. machine, for example, delivers only 0.01 microamperes at 30 Bev!

New ideas of obtaining clashing beams of particles, especially of positive and negative electrons, are also being discussed, as well as being tested on a small scale. Such experiments may be extremely valuable in yielding information on the validity of the method of determining electric and magnetic structure from electron-scattering experiments.

It is clear from this brief study of present-day experiments that higher-energy and higher-intensity accelerators will play an important part in future nuclear physics. Larger machines, however, demand larger-scale efforts from engineers, physicists, administrators, and the public. A glance at the table of large machines shows how costly accelerators have become in terms of both effort and money. Notwithstanding this observation, however, another glance over the long list of accelerators throughout the world will show with what importance accelerators must be regarded. This situation raises one of the most difficult problems confronting the high-energy nuclear physicist today. As one of the foremost machine planners in the United States said recently: "A disturbing phase of our progress into the presently feasible (that is, of the order of 300 to 1000 Bev) range of particle energies is that the equipment is so large and costly as to require difficult decisions of national and even international policy to finance its construction and use." A. M. Weinburg, Director of Oak Ridge National Laboratory, said in a lecture given before the American Rocket Society in May, 1961, ". . . Big Science is an inevitable stage in the development of science and, for better or worse, it is here to stay. . . . When history looks at the twentieth century, she will see science and technology as its theme; she will find in the monuments of Big Science—the huge rockets, the high-energy accelerators, the high-flux research reactors—symbols of our time just as surely as she finds in Notre Dame a symbol of the Middle Ages. She might even see analogies between our motivations for building these tools of giant science and the motivations of the church builders and the pyramid builders. We build our monuments in the name of scientific truth, they built theirs in the name of religious truth; we use our Big Science to add to our country's prestige, they used their churches for their cities' prestige; we build to placate . . . a scientific caste, they built to please the priests of Isis and Osiris."

a review

"CLASSICAL" VS. "MODERN" PHYSICS

In almost every university-physics curriculum, one finds courses called *classical mechanics, electricity and magnetism,* and *optics.* The contents of these courses, which present the view of nature generally accepted before about 1900, nowadays are termed *classical* physics. In the classical view, all matter was composed of *particles,* whose motions obeyed the famous three laws of Newtonian mechanics first formulated by Isaac Newton, in 1686. The essential feature of a particle was that it had no dimensions, so that at every instant it could be thought to lie at a definite point in space. Any particle lying in the plane of this page, for instance, could be completely located by giving it so-called coordinates. These are its perpendicular distances from two lines, called the axes, crossing one another at right angles. Generally, the axes are referred to as horizontal and vertical, and they may be, for instance, the bottom edge and left-hand edge of this page. A particle not in the plane of this paper would require an additional coordinate, which would be its perpendicular height above or below the plane, for its location. The coordinates could be numbers, in terms of some particular unit such as the centimeter, or they might be merely specified algebraically by the symbols x, y, z. The fact that these three coordinates x, y, z are sufficient to locate every particle in space is expressed by the assertion that space is three dimensional.

Classical mechanics

The complete history of any particle is given by the way in which the coordinates change with respect to time. As we know well, the rate at which the particle moves or changes its position with respect to time is termed velocity. There are, therefore, three components to a particle's velocity corresponding to the rates of change of the three coordinate positions with respect to time. Similarly, there are three possible component accelerations, each being given by the rate at which each velocity component changes with respect to time. The analysis of the motion or the trajectory of a particle at different times, depending upon initial conditions of position and motion of the particle and subject to variants of acceleration, is a subject of physics known as *kinematics*. This subject was first developed by Galileo, and Newton incorporated it into the wider subject of dynamics. The distinction between dynamics and kinematics is that, in dynamics, the accelerations of a particle are related to forces. According to Newton's first law, a body can be accelerated only by subjecting it to a force. On the other hand, in general, a finite force produces no more than a finite acceleration; it takes time for a body to change its velocity by any significant amount. This property that all bodies have of *resisting* sudden changes in velocity is known as *inertia*. In fact, according to Newton's second law, the ratio of the force F (along any direction) acting on a particle and giving the resulting acceleration a (along that direction), is a constant, termed the mass m. In algebraic language, the second law reads $F = ma$, or force equals mass times acceleration. This means that, if the force on a particle is doubled, its acceleration is correspondingly doubled, so that the ratio of force to acceleration remains unchanged. Clearly, mass is a measure of inertia. Actually, according to Newton's law of gravitation, the masses of particles are proportional to their weights, that is, to the forces experienced by the particles on the gravitational field of the earth (usually measured by a spring type of weighing scale). A man exerting the same force on particles weighing 1 and 2 pounds, respectively, will give the 2-pound particle exactly ½ the acceleration he gives the 1-pound particle; the 2-pound particle, weighing twice as much, also has twice the inertia of the 1-pound particle.

Associated with every particle, therefore, is a mysterious number, its mass, whose value remains unchanged or, as physicists like to say, is *conserved* as the particle's position changes with time. What happens, however, when particles of classical mechanics sometimes combine to form new particles, as for example, when 2 molecules of hydrogen and 1 molecule of oxygen combine to form 2 molecules of water? Careful measurements on this and other chemical reactions during the classical era showed that the total mass after the reaction always equaled the total mass before reaction; that is, 2 molecules of water formed in the above reaction weighed the same as the 2 molecules of hydrogen plus 1 molecule of oxygen.

The statement of Newton's second law, in the way it has just been given, is true only within the confines of classical physics. We shall have reason later to point out the difference between classical and modern physics, but at this stage it is only fair to admit that Newton, in his profound wisdom, stated his second law in a way that is valid even today in our era of modern physics. His statement amounted to the effect that the ratio of force to the rate of change of momentum (rather than to acceleration, which is the rate of change of velocity) is a constant. The concept of momentum is also fundamental.

Momentum is the product of mass and the velocity of the particle and is commonly associated with the idea of the "way" of a body, that is, the difficulty one feels in trying to bring a moving body to rest. One of the most general and significant conservation laws is that of the conservation of momentum. Conservation of total momentum is exactly what one expects whenever one body acts on another, as in a collision, or even in a reaction in which the bodies become changed, as, for example, in the chemical reaction we have been discussing.

Newton's laws also predict that, when a force acts on a particle, the particle's increase in kinetic energy is associated with a decrease in the potential energy stored in the source of the force, so that one can say the sum of the kinetic and potential energies is conserved when a particle moves under the influence of a force. There are, of course, very definite techniques and formulas for computing kinetic and potential energies that are valid only within the limitations of classical physics. Recognizing that heat is simply a form of energy, associated with random-molecular motions, and properly defining potential energy stored in molecules, one showed that total energy, too, was conserved during chemical reactions.

These and related observations were the basis for the complete acceptance of Newtonian mechanics by classical physicists. In addition, the obvious interpretation of mass conservation during chemical reactions was that some particles were composite combinations of more fundamental or *elementary* particles, and indeed it was soon realized that all substances were combinations of about 90 elements, the elementary particles of which were termed atoms. Molecular hydrogen, the form in which hydrogen gas normally occurs in nature, is composed of 2 atoms of the element hydrogen, whose symbol is H; hence molecular hydrogen has the formula H_2. Similarly molecular oxygen, formula O_2, is composed of 2 atoms of the element oxygen, symbolized by O; a molecule of water, formula H_2O, is composed of 2 atoms of hydrogen and 1 of oxygen; the equation denoting the oxidation of hydrogen to form water is: $2H_2 + O_2 \rightarrow 2H_2O$.

Even as early as 1900 there were many reasons to believe that the distance between the 2 H atoms in H_2 could not be zero, so that a molecule of H_2 could hardly be considered dimensionless. More complicated molecules, e.g., H_2O and penicillin, have larger dimensions still. Under many circumstances, however, especially in the case of the simpler molecules, these distances are of no consequence. For example, in a container of gaseous molecular hydrogen, under conditions of normal temperature and pressure where the average distance between the hydrogen molecules is many times larger than the molecular dimensions, the picture of the molecular motions is not seriously affected by supposing each molecule is a point particle located halfway between the two H atoms. In such a container of H_2, therefore, regarding each H_2 molecule as a Newtonian particle is a convenience, which does not conflict with one's recognition that the H_2 molecule is not strictly dimensionless. What about the H *atoms,* however, or heavier atoms for that matter? Are they dimensionless particles in the Newtonian sense? Again, even as early as 1900, the observation that, under appropriate circumstances (high pressures and low temperatures), a seemingly monatomic gas like neon or argon would condense into a highly incompressible liquid form, strongly suggested that a collection of atoms could not be put into an arbitrarily small volume, i.e., that atoms, too, were not dimensionless. But even just prior to 1900, when the more elementary particles (electrons, protons, and neutrons, from which all atoms are composed) had not yet been discovered, if a person decided that atoms were not dimensionless, he would have to accept that atoms also were composite. To the classical physicists of that era, it was inconceivable that an object could occupy a definite non-zero (finite) volume and be indivisible; it is almost (though not quite) inconceivable to the more blasé physicists of today. In fact, the physicist of pre-1900 seemed forced to believe that

Periodic table (arranged as three panels).

Period 1

I	0
H 1	He 2

Periods 2–3

I	II	III	IV	V	VI	VII	0
Li 3	Be 4	B 5	C 6	N 7	O 8	F 9	Ne 10
Na 11	Mg 12	Al 13	Si 14	P 15	S 16	Cl 17	A 18

Periods 4–7

I	II	III	IVa	Va	VIa	VIIa	VIII			Ia	IIa	IIIa	IV	V	VI	VII	0
K 19	Ca 20	Sc 21	Ti 22	V. 23	Cr 24	Mn 25	Fe 26	Co 27	Ni 28	Cu 29	Zn 30	Ga 31	Ge 32	As 33	Se 34	Br 35	Kr 36
Rb 37	Sr 38	Y 39	Zr 40	Nb 41	Mo 42		Ru 44	Rh 45	Pd 46	Ag 47	Cd 48	In 49	Sn 50	Sb 51	Te 52	I 53	Xe 54
Cs 55	Ba 56	*		Ta 73	W 74		Os 76	Ir 77	Pt 78	Au 79	Hg 80	Tl 81	Pb 82	Bi 83	Po 84		Rn 86.
	Ra 88	Ac 89	Th 90		U 92												
		* La 57	Ce 58	Pr 59	Nd 60		Sm 62		Gd 64	Tb 65		Ho 67	Er 68	Tm 69	Yb 70		

(The VIII columns are bracketed together and marked ↔ VIII.)

~ 136 ~

Periodic System of Elements

Only those elements discovered by 1900, or before, are given in this classification of the elements. Every element is represented by a characteristic symbol and a number, known as its atomic number. The classification is known as the periodic system and was first suggested by Mendeleef. Certain periods are apparent when the elements are arranged according to their chemical similarities—elements in vertical columns, or in columns connected by sloping lines, are in the same chemical families. The periods from 3 to 10 and 11 to 18 are known as short periods, and those from 19 to 36, 37 to 54, and 55 to 86 are known as long periods.

The star (*) at number 57 contains a series from 57 to 71, known as the rare earth series, which must all be squeezed into the position at 57 in order to show the chemical similarities of the remaining members of the third long period. The whole puzzle of the arrangement of atoms in the periodic system was cleared up following the Rutherford-Bohr theory of the atom and the recognition of the exclusion principle by Pauli.

Elements 43, 61, 85, and 87 were discovered after artificially radioactive nuclei were produced. Element 72, hafnium, was discovered in 1923; element 75, rhenium, in 1925; element 91, protoactinium, in 1921; element 63, europium, in 1901; element 66, dysprosium, in 1907; and element 71, lutecium, in 1908. The transuranic elements, with atomic numbers greater than 92 were discovered subsequent to 1940. Elements with atomic numbers greater than 83 are naturally radioactive.

any body occupying a finite volume, if divided in half and these portions divided in half again, etc., would be infinitely (indefinitely) divisible, since, if one stopped after any finite number of divisions, the remaining portions still would have a finite (albeit very small) volume.

By the end of the nineteenth century, even many of the most well-known physicists believed that all the important laws of physics had been discovered and that all one had to do was "to investigate the next decimal place." The above paragraph shows that they should at least have realized that the more elementary components of atoms still awaited discovery. Actually, however, many other difficulties or "unsolved problems" existed in the classical view of nature, as most of the great physicists circa 1900 well realized. For example, just as mysterious as the fact that all bodies had inertia was Newton's observation, thoroughly proved by experiment, that (as we have explained) the acceleration a body received under a given force bore a definite relationship to the body's weight, i.e., to the gravitational forces it felt and was capable of exerting. It was this relation, termed the equality of *inertial* and *gravitational* mass, which Einstein attempted to make less mysterious in his famous theory of general relativity, first put forth in 1915.

Classical electricity and magnetism

To make it quite obvious that the equality of inertial and gravitational mass really is mysterious, we must also discuss the classical theories of *electricity and magnetism*. Newton's law of gravitation states that the gravitational force between any two particles is proportional to the product of their masses divided by the square of the distance between the two particles. (In the equation form of the law, there is also a constant of proportionality that is the same for all bodies and is the so-called universal constant of gravitation.) The physicist of 1900 knew that gravitational forces were not the only forces in nature, however. As mentioned in Chapter Three, a plastic rod (for example, a comb) held above a piece of paper, exerts no discernible gravitational force on it, but, if the comb is rubbed, it is able to lift the paper, thus showing that being rubbed somehow enables the comb to exert a force that is very large compared to its gravitational force. Such a peculiarly endowed comb is termed *electrified,* and experiments as early as 1780 showed that the electric forces between bodies could be understood by assuming the bodies carried *charged* particles. During the eighteenth century, Coulomb showed that the electric force between two charged particles is proportional to the product of the charges on the particles divided by the square of the distance separating the two particles. (Again, in the equation form of this law, there is a constant of proportionality that is a universal constant for all bodies and is referred to as the electric permittivity of space.) Electric force has exactly the same dependence on charge and distance as gravitational force has on mass and distance. Even more striking was the observation that, in any system of particles, the total charge, like the total mass, always seemed to be conserved. In other words, *charge* seemed to play the same role in electric forces as *mass* played in gravitational forces. However, electric forces between bodies bore no discernible relationship to their inertial masses, that is, to the manner in which forces accelerated them.

Magnets also exert forces—on other magnets and on unmagnetized pieces of iron. It was found, soon after the Coulomb experiments in electricity, that the forces between magnets could be understood by assuming that between every pair of magnetic poles there was a force proportional to the product of the so-called pole strengths of the magnetic poles divided by the square of the distance between the poles. (In the equation form of this law, too, there is a constant of proportional known as the magnetic permeability of space. It may be mentioned parenthetically that these three constants —gravitation, permittivity, and permeability—are not just merely numbers but do depend on physical quantities such as mass, length, and time. Their numerical values also depend upon the system in which the forces and other quantities are measured.) Again, the law of force between magnets depends on pole strengths and distance in exactly the same way as the electrostatic force depends on charges and distance, and the force of gravitation depends on mass and distance. To magnetic forces, as to electric forces, the masses of the interacting bodies appear to be wholly irrelevant.

Experiment indicates there are two kinds of magnetic poles, termed north and south; an example of a north pole is the pole pointing north on a compass constructed from a free-floating magnetized needle. North poles attract south poles, but two south poles or two north poles repel each other. Similarly, there are two kinds of electric charges, termed positive and negative. Positive charges attract negative charges; two positive charges or two negative charges repel each other. However, although it is perfectly possible to produce an isolated charge of one sign or the other (for example, a comb rubbed with cat's fur is usually negative), it has been impossible to find an isolated magnetic north or south pole. All magnets have two poles, of opposite character. [If one were to try to be tricky, and one managed to make each end of a long magnetized needle a north pole (which is certainly possible), a south pole would appear at the needle's center.] The problem of why magnetic poles do not appear singly had already been solved by about 1825: Magnetic forces are produced solely by electric currents. A closed loop of wire carrying an electric current produces the same magnetic effects as a magnet whose north pole lies on one side of the loop and whose south pole lies on the other side. It is clear that producing an isolated magnetic pole is no more possible than producing a sheet of paper with only one side. Moreover, it was discovered, also in about 1820, that currents not only produce magnetic fields but also experience forces in magnetic fields, thereby making possible the electric motor. The forces on positive and negative currents are opposite in direction, so that one can identify the sign of an unknown current simply by observing the direction of its deflection in a known magnetic field; this is the method by which today's physicists distinguish the positive from the negative and neutral particles produced in nuclear reactions (see the figures on page 12 and 35), and was of course the way Anderson proved he had discovered a *positive* electron (Chapter One). Although the nature of an electric current was not entirely clear even by 1900, it did seem likely that all currents and, therefore, all magnetic fields were produced by moving electric charges.

The laws of classical electricity and magnetism were put into precise mathematical form by Maxwell, in 1862. Maxwell then showed these laws implied that accelerating electric charges always emitted or *radiated* electromagnetic waves, which moved out from the radiating source with a velocity (in free space) of 3×10^{10} centimeters per second. This prediction, including the magnitude of the wave velocity, followed from Maxwell's equations (and the known strengths of electric and magnetic forces) without any further assumptions. Now it was known that light traveled with a velocity of 3×10^{10} centimeters per second, and experiments (by Hertz) soon showed that accelerated charges did indeed radiate. It was natural, therefore, to conclude that light was, in fact, an electromagnetic wave of the type predicted by Maxwell; indeed, this elucidation of the nature of light was one of the greatest triumphs of classical physics. To put it differently, *optics* (the study of light) and *electricity and magnetism* were, before Maxwell, unrelated subjects; after Maxwell, optics was merely a branch of electricity and magnetism. Parenthetically, we remark that Maxwell's assertion—that all charged particles radiate energy when they are accelerated—was the reason that

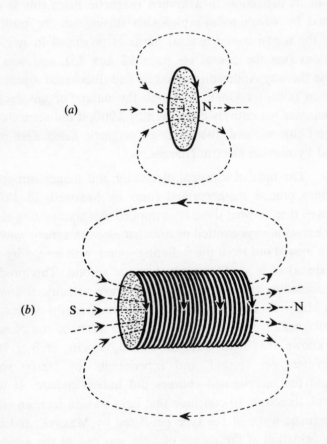

Magnetic Fields

Diagram (a) shows the equivalence between a single, small (in dimensions) current loop (solid line) and a pair of infinitesimally separated north and south poles, forming a so-called magnetic dipole. If one visualizes the loop as being perpendicular to the plane of the paper with the current direction as shown, the equivalent north pole is to the right of the loop and the equivalent south pole to the left.

The dotted lines, through each point in space, running from south to north inside the loop, but north to south outside the loop, show the direction in which an isolated north pole (if it could be found) would move if placed outside the loop at that point. Note that these so-called lines of magnetic force all close and thread the original current loop (as illustrated for two of the lines).

The field around a single atom of iron is very much like that of a magnetic dipole. If a current passes in the same direction through a large length of closely spaced loops, as it would if the wire had the shape of a tightly coiled spring, as in (b), the resultant magnetic lines of force are identical with those observed for an ordinary bar magnet of the same length as the spring. In this way, one infers that the bar magnet consists of a collection of iron atoms somehow aligned so that the magnet contains more equivalent dipoles with north poles on the right than on the left.

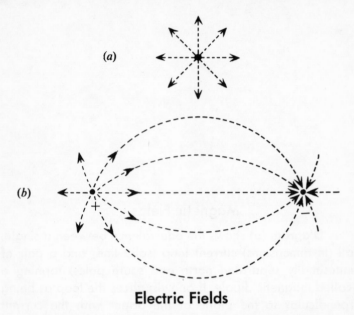

(a)

(b)

Electric Fields

In (a), lines of electric force around an isolated positive charge are shown. The line through any point shows the direction a second positive charge would move if placed at that point. In this simple case, these *electric-field* lines begin at the original positive charge and go out to infinity as straight lines.

In (b) the presence of an equally large but opposite-in-sign, negative, charge has distorted the lines shown in (a). Now every line that leaves the + charge ends in the negative charge. The electric-field lines do not close, however, as did the magnetic-field lines. This nonclosure means the electric-field lines always have sources (where they start) and sinks (where they end), or else go out or come in from infinity. The sources can be consistently interpreted as positive charges, the sinks as negative charges.

The magnetic field lines in the preceding illustration have no sources or sinks, however, and so it is not possible ever to reproduce an observed distribution of magnetic-field lines without using an equal number of north and south poles.

classical physicists found it difficult to believe a hydrogen atom consisted of an electron circling a proton. A circling electron is changing the x, y, or z component of its velocity; therefore, it is continually losing energy by radiation and thus must soon fall into the proton.

Difficulties with classical interpretations

Actually, Maxwell related electricity and magnetism not only to optics but also (in a sense) to mechanics. We have seen that classical physics found it natural to think of material bodies as being infinitely divisible. The theory of infinite divisibility, that is, of *continuous* media, predicts that waves will propagate in such media, and waves of many varieties are actually observed in nature. The essential feature of a wave in classical theory is that it represents a cooperative motion of the medium in which the wave is progressing. This cooperative phenomenon is produced by the motions of the myriads of particles in the medium, but the particle motions may be very different from the wave motion one observes. In the case of a light wave visualized by Maxwell, with the wave progressing to the right, as in the figure on page 146, the electric field at a point increases and decreases with time, exactly as shown in the accompanying figure. The magnetic field also increases and decreases, though in a direction perpendicular to the electric field (and to the direction in which the wave progresses). Hence the assertion that light is an electromagnetic wave. But, if light is a wave, it has to be transported by some medium, says the classical physicist! It is impossible, he says, that an empty vacuum can engage in cooperative vibrations. And so the classical physicist concluded that all space was filled with a mysterious all-pervading *something* called the ether, in which the earth, sun, and stars moved and whose vibrations were sensed by us as light.

Clarification of the properties of the ether and determination of the velocity with which the earth moved through the ether were two famous, unsolved classical problems. Another classical problem was to discover why atoms radiate only certain light frequencies, instead of radiating all frequencies. It was known that relatively long-wavelength low-frequency light appears red to the eye, and that relatively short-wavelength high-frequency light appears blue-violet. Other colors result from light of intermediate frequencies impinging on the

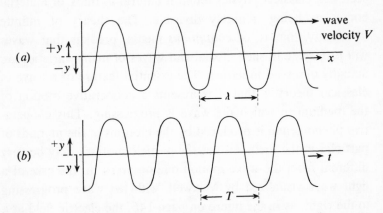

Waveform of Particle Positions

As the wave in (a) moves to the right with wave velocity V, particles move up and down—in a direction perpendicular to the wave velocity. The diagram can be thought of as a snapshot of the particle positions at any one instant, but the same diagram as in (b) also represents the vertical position y(t) of any one particle as a function of time. For the simple waveform shown, the wavelength λ is the distance between successive troughs at one instant, and the period T is the time it takes one particle to execute a complete oscillation (from minimum y to maximum y and back to minimum).

Thus one sees that $V = \lambda/T$. The frequency f is defined as to 1/T, so one also has $V = f\lambda$. For visible light, λ typically is about 5×10^{-5} centimeter, and f is about 10^{15} cycles per second.

eye. But certain atoms favor certain colors, as advertising manufacturers know. Neon lights are characteristically red; the same tubes filled with hydrogen are blue; the characteristic yellow light of a gas flame results from omnipresent atoms of sodium. More careful analysis shows that the radiated light from sodium is not a band of frequencies with a maximum in the yellow, but instead is sharply concentrated at what is essentially a single frequency or *line* (from its appearance in a spectroscope); other atoms behave similarly. Because it is impossible to construct a sensible model of an atom, if accelerated charges necessarily radiate, and also because of a host of other reasons, classical physics provided a completely insufficient basis from which to explain radiation of lines from atoms.

Einstein's interpretation of mechanics

With this very brief review we have tried to show: first, that classical physics was very successful in explaining a great variety of mechanical, electromagnetic, and optical phenomena; second, that these explanations left unsolved many problems and introduced others. In 1900 one would still hope that *classical* explanations of these unsolved problems would be found. But, in 1905, Einstein struck the death knell of these hopes. In his so-called *special* theory of relativity, he showed the falsity of our intuitive notions that space and time are distinct and different concepts. We are immersed not in a three-dimensional space, but in a four-dimensional space-time. Two observers moving relative to each other have altogether different estimates of distance, time, and velocity, as can only be understood by abandoning traditional views that *time is time* and *space is space*. Einstein further showed that there probably was no such medium as an ether; what was perhaps worse, if there were an ether, there would be no way of observing it. One implication of Einstein's special-relativity theory is that the deflection of a moving charged particle in a magnetic field is a natural consequence of the law describing the force experienced by a charged particle in an electric field. From his fundamental postulate that, although it is possible to measure one's velocity relative to another moving body, it is impossible to decide which of two bodies is truly "at rest" relative to free space, Einstein could infer the existence of magnetic forces simply from the knowledge of the existence of electric forces. This achievement indicates the power and beauty of Einstein's theory. Finally, special relativity also implied that mass and energy were interrelated. Material bodies, in their masses, possessed concentrated energy in amounts given by his famous formula $E = mc^2$. When an atom radiates light, which comes off as energy, it necessarily loses some mass. Gone are the separate principles of mass and energy conservation, which classical chemistry supposedly demonstrated! Arrived is a unified principle of mass-energy conservation! Alternatively, we may speak either of mass conservation or of energy conservation, with energy regarded as a form of mass, or mass regarded as a form of energy. Actually, Einstein's formula shows that the mass imbalance in ordinary chemical reactions is too small to be measurable, so classical chemistry does seem to conserve energy and mass separately. But in nuclear reactions, significant mass imbalances and consequent extremely large energy imbalances are possible. The A-bomb era was foreshadowed.

Origins of the quantum theory

Einstein struck another knell of dying classical physics in 1905. In his paper on the photoelectric effect, he showed that light, although a *wave* according to classical physics, actually had *particle-like* properties. We shall not discuss the photoelectric effect in detail but shall simply say it refers to the following observation: Under appropriate circumstances, when light shines on one metallic surface separated from a second metallic surface, current flows between the two surfaces through the space separating them; turn off the light and the current stops. This effect makes possible burglar alarms in banks, conveniently opens doors in supermarkets, and involves the emission of electrons from the metallic surface on which the light beam impinges. Einstein and others have shown that the photoelectric effect and related effects require that the energy and momentum of light be concentrated in *packets, quanta,* or *photons,* as you will. In accordance with Planck's famous assumption, each photon has an energy E, equal to h times the frequency f of the light, and a momentum p equal to h divided by the wavelength λ of the light. The quantity h is Planck's constant, which does not appear in any of the formulas of classical physics. The phrase particle-like properties refers to the fact that, in interactions between electrons and light, the deflection of an electron can be described just as if the electron has collided with a particle of light whose energy E and momentum p were given by

$$E = hf$$
$$p = hf/c = h/\lambda$$

In this picture, the electron-light interaction is visualized as not very different from the collision of two billiard balls on a billiard table, except that the dimensions of the colliding particles—photon and electron—are, of course, very very much smaller than the dimensions of *macroscopic* objects like billiard balls.

There is nothing intrinsically wrong with a theory that gives particle-like properties to light radiations; in fact, as long ago as 1670, Newton, himself, had developed such a theory. The difficulty stems from the fact that one and the same entity—light—behaves like a wave in one set of experiments and like a particle in another set. And waves are so different from particles that no one, neither the classical nor the modern physicist, is able to fully visualize a composite-wave-particle entity, although there are, at present, very satisfactory mathematical theories accurately predicting the results of experiments involving light. In other words, whether it is possible to picture a composite wave-particle phenomenon in the only way we can picture anything—namely, in terms of macroscopic objects common to our experience—we now have (as the classical physicists did not) a mathematically consistent theory, called quantum electrodynamics, which correctly predicts that light has wave properties in certain experiments and has particle properties in others. This theory, like Einstein's special-relativity theory, involves very fundamental revisions in classical views of such concepts as particle size, energy, momentum, etc. The necessary revisions are akin to those involved in the conceptually somewhat simpler (though still quite incomprehensible classically) modern theory of particle motions known as quantum mechanics, which we shall come to in a moment.

To make perfectly clear how different waves and particles are, we mention one essential property of waves, namely, interference. Two waves of the same frequency and amplitude, but so adjusted in phase that the crest of one wave reaches a point simultaneously with the trough of the second, completely annul one another at that point (see the diagram on page 151). The effect is easily demonstrated with sound waves, and it can be easily observed in the overlapping ripples arising from two stones thrown into a lake. In fact, wavelengths of light are measured by observing how the point where the waves annul one another shifts as the position between the interfering wave sources is varied. Interference is about as impossible to picture on a particle model of light as it is to explain how two bullets, shot from two different guns toward the same point on a wall, can annul each other so as to produce no mark on the wall. What makes the dual, wave-particle interpretation of light even more puzzling is that the photon properties of energy and momentum must be derived from wave properties, namely, frequency and wavelength. Frequency would appear to have no meaning at all for particles per se, since the magnitude of frequency is found from an experimentally measured wavelength that is based solely on observations of a wave phenomenon—interference.

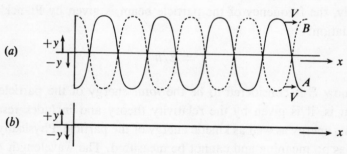

(a)

(b)

Destructive Interference

If a wave A (solid line) is superimposed on wave B (dotted line), the result shown in (b) is as if there had been no waves at all. The two waves have wholly cancelled each other; the physicist says *destructive interference* has occurred. The waves A and B have the same frequency but are a half-cycle out of phase.

Such interference in sound waves would be noticed, for instance, by an observer on a line with two identical and simultaneously struck 440-cycle tuning forks placed about 1.2 feet apart.

Introduction of wave mechanics

The final death blow to classical physics (presaged by Einstein's 1905 knell) was delivered in 1924, when, following a suggestion by de Broglie, it was shown that particle beams—beams of electrons, protons, or hydrogen atoms—had wave properties. In particular, one could demonstrate interference with these particle beams just as unequivocally as the classical physicists had demonstrated interference with light beams 100 years previously. The analogy between light and particles is almost complete. The wavelength of a particle is given by de Broglie's equation:

$$\lambda = h/p$$

where p is the momentum of the particle. This is exactly the same as the equation for the momentum of a photon. Similarly, the frequency of the particle beam is given by Planck's equation:

$$f = E/h$$

if now E is considered to be the *total* energy of the particle; that is, it is given by the relativity theory and includes rest-mass energy as well as kinetic energy of the particle. Physically, f has no meaning and cannot be measured. The wavelength λ, however, has a very definite meaning and can be measured if λ is not too small, i.e., if the momentum p is small enough (note that h is already a small quantity). This may definitely be the case in elementary-particle physics where the masses of the particles are extremely small. As another illustration of the applicability of the equations above, we cite a striking example originally given by de Broglie. If an electron in the Bohr model of the hydrogen atom is conceived to be an electron wave instead of a dynamic particle, the radii of the Bohr orbits can be deduced precisely from the postulate that the circumferences of the orbits shall be exactly equal to integral multiples of the electron wavelengths.

Actually, modern quantum mechanics is a generalization of Newtonian mechanics. Its fundamental formula, the Schrödinger equation (developed in 1926), embodies in a subtle and remarkable way the contents of de Broglie's relations. The Schrödinger equation for a system of particles describes the variation in time of the so-called wave function, which embodies all ascertainable information about the system. Using the Schrödinger equation without ad hoc postulates, such as the one discussed above leading to the radii of Bohr orbits, one completely and quantitatively predicts practically all the properties of the hydrogen atom and also the results of a whole host of other experiments involving the motions of elementary or near-elementary particles, such as electrons and atoms. In fact, the successes of quantum mechanics are so widespread that its essential correctness can hardly be doubted (see, however, the next section). For instance, quantum mechanics predicts the actual line frequencies at which atoms radiate (wholly insoluble by classical physics) with accuracies better than 1 part in a million.

Limitations of quantum mechanics

On the other hand, quantum mechanics, like the special theory of relativity, requires considerable revision of previously accepted classical concepts. For example, according to quantum mechanics, it is impossible to simultaneously prescribe the position *and* velocity of a particle. In fact, the mini-

Portion of More Recent Table of Elements

The system of nuclei of elements—1960 version—follows on pages 154 and 155. Compared with the Table on page 136, it will be seen that elements are now shown as mixtures of nuclei of different masses.

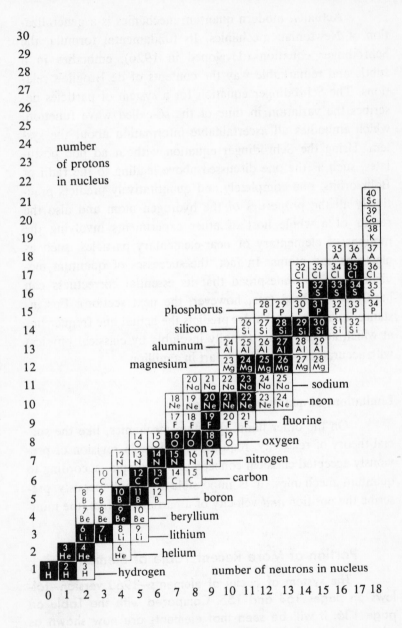

number
of protons
in nucleus

									40 Sc
									39 Ca
									38 K

phosphorus
silicon
aluminum
magnesium
— sodium
— neon
— fluorine
— oxygen
— nitrogen
— carbon
— boron
— beryllium
— lithium
— helium
hydrogen   number of neutrons in nucleus

0 1 2 3 4 5 6 7 8 9 10 11 12 13 14 15 16 17 18

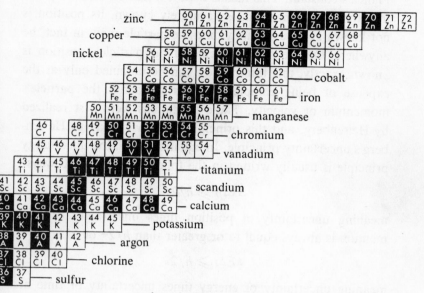

number of neutrons in nucleus

19 20 21 22 23 24 25 26 27 28 29 30 31 32 33 34 35 36 37 38 39 40 41

	mass 000
000 **El**	stable nucleus, element El

	mass 111
111 El	unstable nucleus, element El

mum product of the uncertainties of position and momentum of a particle simultaneously measured is on the order of Planck's constant. This means that, if a particle's velocity and therefore its momentum, is accurately known, its position is not known at all accurately, and the particle may, in fact, be anywhere. On the other extreme, if the particle's position is known exactly, this information can be obtained only at the expense of being completely uncertain about the particle's momentum or velocity. These limitations were first realized by Heisenberg, and this principle is known today as Heisenberg's uncertainty principle. In equation form, the uncertainty principle is usually written in the following alternative ways:

$$\Delta x \Delta p \geqslant h/2\pi$$

meaning uncertainty of position times uncertainty of momentum is always equal to or greater than $h/2\pi$ or

$$\Delta E \Delta t \geqslant h/2\pi$$

meaning uncertainty of energy times uncertainty of time at which the energy is measured is always equal to or greater than $h/2\pi$. It is important to realize that h is a minute quantity, equal to only approximately 6×10^{-27} erg-second, or 6 parts in 1 thousand million million million millionth of an erg multiplied by 1 second. An erg, in itself, is a small bit of kinetic energy, amounting to only that possessed by a particle of mass 2 grams moving with a velocity of 1 centimeter per second. Only in elementary-particle and atomic physics do these uncertainties assume experimental importance.

There is little need to stress the radical departure of uncertainty relations from anything expected classically. Position and velocity were wholly independent quantities classically; a particle could be put anywhere, and one could simultaneously assign it any velocity one wished. Similarly, energy and time were unrelated classically. Another consequence of the description of natural phenomena in terms of quantum mechanics is that nature lost the determinism we had grown accustomed to accepting in classical physics. Given 2 atoms, seemingly identical in every way, it is consistent with quantum mechanics that one atom should radiate immediately and the other atom should not radiate until some later time. According to quantum mechanics, we cannot expect to predict what any one atom will do in such a case, though we can predict that some events (for example, immediate radiation) are more likely than others (such as long-delayed radiation). Similarly, the quantum-mechanical picture of an atom or molecule is as has been shown on page 6. One can predict the relative probability of finding an electron at a point, and can say that the electron is most likely to be found in a certain region (about 5×10^{-9} centimeter from the proton, in the case of atomic hydrogen), but in any given atom one cannot definitely state where the electron will be at any given time.

Limited applicability of classical physics

Let us summarize anew. Classical physics explained a vast quantity of observation, but left many problems unsolved. Modern physics, the developments in physics since 1900, has resolved many classically insoluble problems, but in so doing has also left some problems unsolved. In general, modern physics has not shown classical physics to be "wrong," but rather has shown that classical physics was right in a restricted domain, namely, the domain of the observations known to Newton, Maxwell, and other giants of classical physics. Classical physics really is "incorrect," in the sense that it makes incorrect predictions, in domains outside its original province. For particle velocities typically encountered on earth, Newtonian mechanics is extremely accurate. For particle velocities approaching the velocity of light, the limiting velocity with which any matter or signal can be propagated according to Einstein, one must use Einstein's modifications of Newtonian mechanics. However, these modifications are unimportant, and one would be foolish to encumber one's self with them, when velocities are small compared to 3×10^{10} centimeters per second. Similarly, quantum mechanics is needed for particles of atomic dimensions (about 10^{-8} centimeter) and masses (about 10^{-24} gram). But for bodies of more conventional dimensions and masses, the uncertainties described by Heisenberg's uncertainty principle are utterly insignificant, and one can ignore the quantum-mechanical pronouncement that position and momentum, or energy and time, in describing a particular state of a particle, cannot be independently prescribed. For example, suppose we were to have a particle with a mass of 2 grams and a velocity of 1 centimeter per second. If we were unable to specify where the particle was at a particular instant to an accuracy of better than 10^{-13} centimeter, then according to the uncertainty-principle equation given earlier, we would be unable to specify its velocity at the same instant to an accuracy of better than $(3 \times 10^{-14})/2\pi$ centimeter per second. These accuracies in the specification of a macroscopic particle as massive as 2 grams are, of course, unrealizable in experimental measurement, and this is an instance in which the uncertainty principle has no significance in practice. Now, suppose we were to have an electron in a normal hydrogen atom which we know to be about 10^{-8} centimeter in radius. We have also read that the momentum of the electron in the hydrogen atom, according to de Broglie's ideas, is equal to h divided by the wavelength of the electron, which, in this case is approximately the circumference of the hydrogen atom; that is, the momentum is approximately h divided by $2\pi 10^{-8}$ centimeter. Suppose the uncertainty in momentum is comparatively large, on the order of the momentum itself. Then, according to the uncertainty principle, we argue that the uncertainty in the position of the electron must be equal to or greater than $h/2\pi$ divided by the uncertainty of momentum of $h/2\pi 10^{-8}$. The uncertainty of the electron's position is, therefore, 10^{-8} centimeter. An attempt to determine the momentum more precisely would only increase the uncertainty in the electron position. Thus, on an atomic scale, we are quite uncertain where the electron is within a hydrogen atom. The uncertainty principle has, therefore, a very important meaning in dealing with very light particles encountered in the areas of both atomic and nuclear physics.

"The Untravell'd World"

Today's unsolved problems, like those of 1900 and, very probably, like those of the future, are of two kinds. There are observations to which today's physics seems applicable but makes quantitatively incorrect predictions; there are other observations about which today's physics makes no predictions, because it does not appear applicable. Until Yang and Lee developed their theory, modern physics made quantitatively incorrect predictions about the directions of the spins of electrons emitted in beta decay. No one today is prepared to say how many *inert,* charged, spin $h/4\pi$ mesons there are. Is the μ meson the only such meson, or are there others? Is there some reason why the elementary particle next heavier than the electron is 207 times more massive than the electron but otherwise is very similar to the electron in its properties? No one knows the answer to these questions, nor is it clear that our present theories could answer them without introducing some new far-reaching hitherto-unsuspected principle akin to Pauli's postulate that electrons obey the exclusion principle.

Not only are there two kinds of unsolved problems, but the attitudes of physicists toward presently unanswerable questions are of two sorts. Some physicists believe that all seemingly sensible questions should ultimately be answerable; other physicists think some facts have no explanation other than the whim of the Creator of the universe. Thus there are some who feel it must be possible to prove that the muon, defined as a particle heavier than the electron but otherwise similar in properties, has to possess a mass exactly 207 times the electron mass; there are others who feel the muon mass could have any value, and that we are fortunate there are not 50 particles all resembling electrons and having only slightly different masses. There are some who advocate strong mathematical reasons why there are not nonzero-mass (relatively long-lived) elementary particles of spin $h/2\pi$ (twice the electron spin), and there are others who say, "Let's wait and see; we haven't found all the elementary particles yet." There have been some physicists in the past, notably Eddington, who believed they could predict on purely mathematical grounds the exact number of electrons in the universe. Eddington's value was (136×2^{256}). ("I believe," wrote Eddington, "there are 15,747,724,136,275,002,577,605,653,961,181,555,468,-044,717,914,527,116,709,366,231,425,076,185,631,031,-296 protons in the universe and the same number of electrons.") At present, practically all physicists feel that the total mass of the universe is not predictable, that is, the total mass is indeed a capricious fact of creation.

We note further that, although the unsolved problems mentioned in the previous paragraph have arisen solely as a result of the research of the last 60 years, not all today's unsolved problems are so recent. Many old problems involve gravitation, which despite Einstein's contributions remains almost as puzzling a phenomenon as in the classical era. Can gravitational forces, such as might exist between matter and antimatter, for instance, be repulsive as well as attractive? No one knows, and thus far only attractive gravitational forces have been observed. Are there gravitational waves akin to electromagnetic waves? Again, no one knows, although such waves have been predicted. Can gravitational effects propagate with speeds exceeding the velocity of light? Einstein's theory says they cannot, but no evidence that gravitational effects do not propagate with infinite speeds has ever been discovered.

Now we can say, finally, what this book is about. Physics research since 1900 has had some discernible currents, although one must recognize that physics is remarkable among the sciences for the way a discovery in one area of physics affects thinking in others. One such current is the subject of this book, namely, the attempt to discover all the fundamental particles and to determine the nature of the forces between these particles. This current naturally has led to construction of higher- and higher-energy machines, and it presently looks as if there remains a long (perhaps an infinite) route to follow before all elementary-particle problems are completely solved. As we follow this route, we chart it with proved (so we think) principles. The most reliable principles (so we thought before Yang and Lee) were the conservation laws—of energy, of momentum, of angular momentum or spin, of electric charge, of left-right symmetry (or parity). Hitherto, these principles had no failures and many important successes. For example, knowledge that electron, neutron, and proton have spin $h/4\pi$, combined with conservation of energy, momentum, spin, and charge, implied that beta decay of the neutron must also involve a massless-uncharged spin-$h/4\pi$ particle; merely believing the conservation laws enabled Pauli to predict the existence of the neutrino.

Moreover, the correctness of the above conservation principles (except for charge conservation) had been explained on very general and convincing grounds. Indeed, it had been shown that momentum conservation could be understood on the grounds that the universe had no natural center, that is, no point was a better origin of coordinates than any other point. Energy conservation could be similarly understood on the grounds that the universe had no favored instant from which to start measuring time. Angular momentum conservation was implied by the postulate that there was no favored orientation of the coordinate axes, that is, it did not matter whether one chose the x axis as horizontal or tilted 45° from the vertical. Parity conservation meant one could let the x, y, and z axes correspond, respectively, to the thumb, forefinger, and middle finger (held perpendicular to each other, of course) on the right hand or on the left hand (see the diagram on this page); either correspondence would be equally useful and equally convenient for describing natural phenomena. In the language of this paragraph we also can give a more precise statement of Einstein's fundamental postulate in his special theory of relativity. He asserted that there was no favored origin or orientation of the coordinate axes x, y, z, t in four-dimensional space-time. Physically, this postulate could be

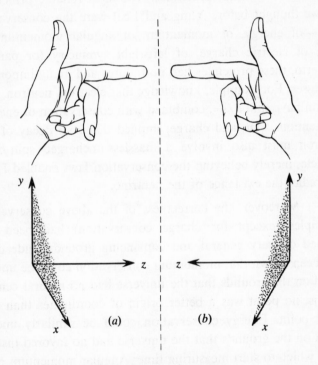

Coordinate Systems

(a) Left-hand coordinate system; (b) right-hand coordinate system. The coordinate system on the left can be thought of as the reflection in a mirror (dotted line) of the coordinate system on the right, just as the left hand is the mirror reflection of the right hand.

seen to imply that natural phenomena must be describable identically by any two observers moving at constant speed relative to each other.

We now can begin to appreciate the shock and bewilderment physicists felt when the failure of parity conservation was announced. We can also see why today's physicists have been trying to cast the new information about elementary particles into the always-successful conservation-principle mold. Thus the success of spin conservation suggested the introduction of a quantity *isotopic spin,* supposedly conserved in strong interactions and related to orientation-independence in a mathematical *isotopic spin space.* Similarly, the success of electric-charge conservation suggests introducing the strangeness number. On the other hand, our experience with classical physics also suggests that we can go just so far in extending previously successful theoretical procedures into new domains. New fundamental ideas may be needed that may possibly be even more alarming to our intuitions about space, time, length, velocity, energy, etc., than were relativity and quantum mechanics to the classical physicists. But, until such theories are developed or shown to be unnecessary, no one can even guess what the ultimate resolution of today's problems will be. That is a part of the fascination of high-energy physics —that completely untraveled world, the world that lies beyond the edge of our normal experience of biological and chemical processes, yet a world that, by its interaction with the fundamental forces of nuclear physics, gives us a deeper appreciation of the nuclei we are trying to understand.

appendix

WORLD LIST
OF ACCELERATORS

This list comprises all types of machines, either in operation or in the course of construction at the end of 1958. The size refers to the diameter of the magnetic-pole face, and the orbit radius refers to the radius of the magnetic ring. The particles normally accelerated in the machines are protons (p), deuterons (d), or heavy ions (h), unless otherwise stated. The information contained herein is based on a report by F. T. Howard (Oak Ridge National Laboratory Report 2644).

Fixed-Frequency Cyclotrons

Country	Size, inches	Energy, Mev	Usual beam particle
Australia			
Canberra	31	8	p
Melbourne	40	11	p
Belgium	40	13	d
Bulgaria	47	12.5	d
China	47	12.5	d

Fixed-Frequency Cyclotrons (continued)

Country	Size, inches	Energy, Mev	Usual beam particle
Czechoslovakia	47	12.5	d
Denmark	35	12	d
France			
Orsay	30	7	d
Orsay	79	20	d
Saclay	70	22	d
Germany, East	47	12.5	d
Germany, West	40	13	d
Israel	16	2	p
Japan			
Kyoto	41	15	d
Osaka	44	12	d
Tokyo	63	21	d
Tokyo	25	4	d
Tokyo	16	2	d
Netherlands	33	12	p
Poland	20	—	—
	47	12.5	d
Rumania	47	12.5	d
Sweden	31	7	d
	89	22	d
Switzerland	33	14	d
South Africa	45	16	d
U.S.S.R.			
Dubna	120	100	h
Kiev	—	14	d
Leningrad	30	4	d
Leningrad	47	12.5	d
Leningrad	47	25	h
Leningrad	14	2	d
Moscow	59	22	d
Moscow	47	14	d
United Kingdom			
Birmingham	40	12	d
Birmingham	62	20	d
Liverpool	36	9	d
London	50	15	d

Fixed-Frequency Cyclotrons (continued)

Country	Size, inches	Energy, Mev	Usual beam particle
U.S.A.			
Ann Arbor, Mich.	42	10	d
Ann Arbor, Mich.	64	40	d
Argonne, Ill.	62	22	d
Berkeley, Cal.	72	24	d
Berkeley, Cal.	88	115	p
Birmingham, Ala.	16	4	p
Bloomington, Ind.	45	12	d
Boulder, Col.	52	30	p
Brookhaven, N.Y.	18	3	p
Brookhaven, N.Y.	62	20	d
Cambridge, Mass.	43	16	d
Cleveland, Ohio	60	20	d
Columbus, Ohio	47	12	d
Corvallis, Ore.	37	7.5	d
East Lansing, Mich.	83	40	d
Lafayette, Ind.	37	10	d
Livermore, Cal.	90	15	p
Los Alamos, N.M.	42	16	d
Los Angeles, Cal.	44	50	p
New Haven, Conn.	28	4	d
New York, N.Y.	36	15	p
Oak Ridge, Tenn.	44	5	p
Oak Ridge, Tenn.	63	27	h
Oak Ridge, Tenn.	76	75	p
Oak Ridge, Tenn.	86	25	p
Pittsburgh, Pa.	47	20	d
Rochester, N.Y.	26	8	p
St. Louis, Mo.	45	10	d
Seattle, Wash.	60	22	d
Stanford, Cal.	27	3	d
Urbana, Ill.	44	14	p
Washington, D.C.	60	16	d
Yugoslavia			
Zagreb	56	16	d

Frequency-Modulated Cyclotrons

Country	Size, inches	Energy, Mev	Usual beam particle
Argentina	71	30	d
Canada	82	100	p
CERN[a]	197	600	p
France	110	155	p
Germany, West	75	33	d
Netherlands	71	28	d
Sweden	90	200	p
U.S.S.R.	236	680	p
United Kingdom			
Harwell	110	175	p
Liverpool	156	400	p
U.S.A.			
Berkeley, Cal.	189	730	p
Cambridge, Mass.	95	168	p
Chicago, Ill.	170	460	p
Los Angeles, Cal.	41	21	p
Nevis, N.Y.	164	385	p
Pittsburgh, Pa.	141	440	p
Princeton, N.J.	35	20	p
Rochester, N.Y.	130	240	p

[a] CERN is the European Organization for Nuclear Research located in Geneva. In 1960 to 1962, the contributing countries and the percentage financial contributions to the organization were: Austria (1.93), Belgium (4.15), Denmark (1.99), France (21.22), West Germany (19.52), Greece (1.17), Italy (10.09), Netherlands (3.85), Norway (1.61), Sweden (4.23), Switzerland (3.29), United Kingdom (25.00), Yugoslavia (1.95). The total budget for 1960 was 65 million Swiss francs ($13,000,000).

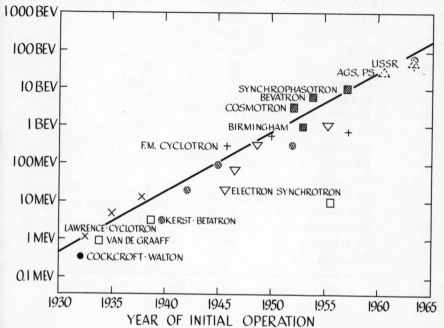

PARTICLE ACCELERATOR DEVELOPMENT

Accelerator Energies

Energies of high-energy-particle accelerators throughout the world have increased by a factor of approximately ten every five years starting from 1932. At this rate, 1000 Bev should be reached by about 1973.

In this chart, a particular type of accelerator is indicated by a special symbol: x = fixed-frequency cyclotron, starting with the Lawrence cyclotron in 1932; + = frequency-modulated cyclotron, beginning with the Berkeley machine in 1946; ▨ = proton, weak-focusing synchrotron, beginning with the Cosmotron in 1952; △ = alternating-gradient synchrotron, phasosynchrotron, originating with the CERN and Brookhaven machines in 1959 and 1960.

Proton Synchrotrons

Country	Radius, feet	Energy, Gev	Type[a]
Australia	15.7	10.6	CG
CERN	328	30	AG
France	27.5	3	CG
Netherlands	10.7	1	CG
U.S.S.R.			
Dubna	89	10	CG
Leningrad	16.4	0.65	AG
Leningrad	547	50	AG
Moscow	131	7	AG
United Kingdom			
Birmingham	16.4	1	CG
Harwell	62	7	CG
U.S.A.			
Argonne, Ill.	71	12.5	CG
Brookhaven, N.Y.	30	3	CG
Brookhaven, N.Y.	421	33	AG
Berkeley, Cal.	50	6.2	CG
Princeton, N.J.	30	3	CG

[a] CG = conventional gradient; AG = alternating gradient

Electron Synchrotrons

Country	Radius, feet	Energy, Gev	Type[a]
Germany, West			
Bonn	5.6	0.5	CG
Hamburg	29.5	7.5	AG
Italy	11.8	1.2	CG
Japan	13.1	1.3	AG
Sweden	12	1.2	AG
U.S.S.R.	1.1	1	CG
U.S.A.			
Cambridge, Mass.	86	6	AG
Ithaca, N.Y.	12.5	1.5	CG
Pasadena, Cal.	12.3	1.2	CG

[a] CG = conventional gradient; AG = alternating gradient

Electron Linear Accelerators

Country	Length, feet	Energy, Gev
U.S.A.		
Stanford, Cal.	220	1
Stanford, Cal.	10,500	45
France		
Orsay	330	1

Proton Linear Accelerators

Country	Length, feet	Energy, Mev
Poland	—	10
U.S.S.R.		
Kharkov	40.6	21
United Kingdom		
Harwell	—	50
U.S.A.		
Berkeley, Cal.	20	10
Brookhaven, N.Y.	110	50
Los Angeles, Cal.	41	32
Minnesota	98	68

Heavy-Ion Linear Accelerators

Country	Length, feet	Energy, Mev
U.S.S.R.	—	100
United Kingdom	90	100
U.S.A.		
Berkeley, Cal.	105	100
New Haven, Conn.	105	100

GLOSSARY

Alpha particle: A helium nucleus, approximately four times the mass of a proton, which is emitted from a nucleus when it undergoes alpha decay.

Ampere: A unit of electric current. Since 1950, by international agreement, the ampere is defined in terms of the attractive force that occurs between two conductors carrying this current. The attractive force can be interpreted on the basis of magnetic forces—one conductor carrying a current generates a magnetic field at the other conductor, and the current flowing in this second conductor is then influenced by this magnetic field. The current flowing through a 100-watt bulb in an ordinary 110-volt house circuit is about 1 ampere.

Antiparticle: In our ordinary universe, many fundamental particles exist in only one form; for example, a negative electron, a positive proton. From the requirement that all physical laws are assumed to be consistent with Einstein's special theory of relativity (or, as physicists say, are relativistically invariant), Dirac was led to predict that there would be antiparticle *images* of ordinary particles. When the ordinary particle has a charge, the antiparticle has the opposite sign of charge; for instance, the antielectron is a positron and an antiproton is a negatively charged proton. When the particle has no charge, as in the ordinary neutron, the antiparticle also has no charge (in this case, however, the antineutron has an opposite magnetic moment from the ordinary neutron). The laws of physics are precisely the same for describing interactions between antiparticles as they are for describing interactions between ordinary particles, and we are not capable of deciding which are the *real* particles and which are the image particles.

Atomic number: The number given an element in the classification of elements. It is the same as the number of protons in the nucleus, or is equal to the magnitude of the nuclear charge in units of the electron's charge. The atomic number is normally denoted by the letter Z. For hydrogen, $Z = 1$. For helium, $Z = 2$. For uranium, $Z = 92$, etc.

Atomic power: Power in physics is defined as the rate of doing useful work. Atomic power is obtained from atomic-, or rather, nuclear-energy sources, such as the fission of uranium in nuclear reactions. Nuclear energy is evolved from the fission of a substance, such as uranium of mass 235 (U^{235}), because it can be broken apart by neutrons into 2 more tightly bound fragments. A typical fission of U^{235} might be as follows:

$$U^{235} + n^1 \rightarrow Ba^{141} + Kr^{92} + 3n^1$$

In this equation, the two fragments, barium of mass 141 and krypton of mass 92, have their component protons and neutrons more strongly bound together than they were in U^{235}. Because these neutrons and protons in the fragments became more tightly packed together than before, energy was released in the process. This energy, in fact, is measurable also as equivalent mass. It can be shown that the sum of the masses of Ba^{141}, Kr^{92}, and 3 neutrons is less than U^{235} and 1 neutron, by approximately one-fifth of a proton mass. The significant factor in the evolution of nuclear energy by the breaking down of massive nuclei is the amount of binding energy per nucleon. The most tightly bound nuclei lie in the region of those elements around iron. Nuclear energy may also be evolved from the synthesis of light nuclei into more massive ones. Such processes occur in thermonuclear reactions taking place, for instance, in the interiors of stars. The most basic stellar reaction (*see* Stellar synthesis of elements) is the production of helium from protons. The mass of 4 protons is approximately $1/40$ of a proton mass heavier than 1 helium nucleus. Most of this energy is released as heat energy in the star's interior when the 4 protons become converted into a helium nucleus. (Neutrinos carry away somewhat less than 10 per cent of the energy liberated.)

Baryon: This is a particle belonging to the heaviest group of particles, which includes the nucleons and hyperons.

Betatron oscillations: Usually small, controlled, oscillations of particles in a circular accelerator. The oscillations occur both in the radial and axial directions about the equilibrium orbit.

Beta particle: An electron, either positively or negatively charged, emitted from a radioactive nucleus.

Billion electric volt (Bev): (*See* Electron volt.) One billion electron volt, as used in this book, is 1 thousand million, that is, 10^9.

Bohr atom: In the Bohr theory of the atom (1913), electrons circulate in orbits about a positively charged nucleus. The forces constraining the electrons in their orbits are the electrostatic (coulomb) forces between the negative charges of the electrons and the positive charge of the nucleus. The new feature of the Bohr atom, which, in fact, launched the whole theory of present-day atomic physics, was that only those electron orbits that satisfied a quantum condition were indeed permitted in nature. This quantum condition was that the amount of orbital angular momentum possessed by an electron could only be an integral multiple of Planck's constant h divided by 2π. (*See* Spin.) Subsequent to 1913, Bohr's theory was subject to a number of modifications and elaborations. Following Schrödinger's development of his *wave equation* in 1926, the Bohr theory description was replaced by more-rigorous quantum-mechanical treatments.

Boson: A generic term describing elementary particles that have zero or 2 units ($2 \times h/4\pi$) of spin. Although the term has not been used in this book, some authors prefer to classify the elementary particles into baryons, leptons, and bosons. The particles that at present constitute the bosons are: K particles (zero spin), π mesons (zero spin), and photons ($h/2\pi$ spin).

Center of mass: The center of mass of a system of particles is a point at which the whole mass can be considered as acting. Generally, for a system of particles moving in the earth's gravitational field, it is the point where the gravitational effects appear to be concentrated. For example, in the case of a broomstick supported horizontally, the center of gravity or of mass is the point at which one can balance the broomstick on a single finger without the stick tilting to one side or the other. For a pair of equal masses, e.g., the H_2 molecule, the center of mass is the point at the center of the line between the two H atoms. For a molecule like CO (carbon monoxide), if the interatomic distance is called L, the center of mass is $(3/7)L$ from the oxygen atom and $(4/7)L$ from the C atom, because oxygen (mass 16) is 4/3 times as heavy as carbon (mass 12).

Center-of-mass system: This is the system of coordinates employed by an observer who places himself, and the origin of coordinates, at the center of mass of a collection of particles. The observer thinks the center of mass (assumed here to be unaccelerated) is at rest, even though to another observer in the laboratory the center of mass may appear to be moving with constant velocity. As a result of this definition, the total momentum of the collection of particles is always zero in the center-of-mass system.

Charge conservation: The net charge in any nuclear reaction remains unchanged. The following are only a few of many illustrations of charge conservation in elementary particle decay:

$$\tau^+ \rightarrow \pi^+ + \pi^- + \pi^+$$
$$\tau^+ \rightarrow \pi^+ + \pi^0 + \pi^0$$
$$\tau^- \rightarrow \pi^- + \pi^+ + \pi^-$$
$$\theta^0 \rightarrow \pi^+ + \pi^-$$
$$\theta^0 \rightarrow \pi^0 + \pi^0$$

Conservation of energy: This is a principle known since about 1850, according to which energy in a closed system of interacting bodies or particles remains constant. According to twentieth-century physics and chemistry, this principle has to be widened to include the conservation of mass and energy together. This change arose with the theory of special relativity in which Einstein showed that mass and energy are interconvertible according to the well-known equation that energy equals the product of mass and the square of the velocity of light (namely, $E = mc^2$).

Cosmic rays: Mainly these are very high energy protons that are incident on the top of the earth's atmosphere from outer space. They have energies up to 10^{19} ev with a very wide energy spread. As cosmic rays penetrate through the earth's atmosphere, the content of the rays is profoundly changed by the interactions of the high-energy particles with the atoms contained in the air. At sea level, most of the high-energy protons have disappeared, and the main components are a *hard* or strongly penetrating high-energy component mainly of μ mesons and a *soft* or weakly penetrating component of electrons.

Coulomb: A unit of electrical charge. One coulomb of charge passing a section in a conductor every second is equivalent to a current of 1 ampere.

Electron: The lightest material particle, mass $= 9.11 \times 10^{-28}$ gram. Electrons are the negatively charged constituents of all atoms.

Electron charge: Charge is atomic in character; that is, there is a smallest amount below which charge may not be divided. This smallest charge e, when negative, resides on certain elementary particles like the electron and antiproton, and when positive, resides on such particles as the positive electron (positron) and the proton.

$$e = 1.6 \times 10^{-19} \text{ coulomb}$$

Electron volt (ev): An energy unit. When a charged particle having a charge equal to the magnitude of the electronic charge, either negative or positive, is accelerated across a gap to which an electrical potential of 1 volt is applied, the energy gained by the particle will be 1 ev:

$$1 \text{ ev} = 1.6 \times 10^{-19} \text{ joule}$$

Elementary particle: This concept has been discussed more particularly in Chapter Two. In low-energy nuclear physics the elementary particles would probably be confined to the photon (γ ray), neutrino (ν), electron (e), proton (p) and neutron (n). The deuteron (H^2) and the alpha particle (He^4) are considered composite particles. In high-energy physics there are many other particles, such as π mesons, hyperons, and antiparticles that are considered elementary. However, it may well be that the term *elementary* has no sensible meaning for fundamental nuclear particles. One theory of fundamental particles is that they are representations of dynamic interactions of other fundamental particles on one another.

Energy: The capacity to do useful work. It may be kinetic energy, which is energy of motion, or potential energy, which is some potential form, such as gravitational, chemical, electrical, or atomic. As discussed in conservation of energy, mass is also convertible into energy. (*See also* Mass-energy.)

Erg: A unit of energy. 1 erg $= 10^{-7}$ joule. Also, 1000 joules $=$ 1 kilowatt $\times$ 1 second.

Exclusion principle (Pauli principle): The formal statement of this principle is that the wave function describing any collection of electrons changes sign when the positions and spins of any two electrons are interchanged. It can be shown that this statement implies no two electrons in any one system can be identical in their quantum-mechanical state. Electrons in an atom are described by *quantum numbers,* and there are 4 quantum numbers which fully specify an electron in an atom. Thus no two electrons can have the same set of 4 quantum numbers. The arrangement of atoms in the periodic system can be beautifully explained on the basis of this principle. There is no classical description of Pauli's principle.

Fission: Nuclei of many of the heaviest atoms, uranium, for example, may divide either spontaneously or upon excitation into parts of more or less comparable size. (*See* Atomic power.)

Gamma (γ) ray: An electromagnetic radiation of the same nature as x rays and light rays but of much higher frequency and much shorter wavelength. Gamma rays may be very energetic and are generally very much more penetrating than x rays.

Gauss: A unit of magnetic induction. The force on a charged particle moving perpendicularly to a magnetic field is directly proportional to the product of magnetic induction, the charge on the particle, and the velocity of the particle. The earth's magnetic field at the surface of the earth is about 1 gauss.

Geiger counter: An electric device invented by Geiger and Rutherford for counting individual charged particles. The counter consists of a wire stretched down the axis of a metal outer cylinder which contains gas at approximately 1/10 atmosphere pressure. A high voltage of several hundred volts is connected to the wire. When an ionizing particle enters the gas between the cylinder and the wire, the gas insulation is broken and a sudden surge of charge is collected on the wire. The entry of a single particle into the sensitive region is thereby recorded as an electric "kick."

Giga electron volt (Gev): Same as Bev.

h; **Planck's constant:** This constant characteristically appears in quantum physics but has no place in classical physics. It was introduced in 1900 by the German physicist, Max Planck, in order to explain the nature of radiation emitted by a heated body. The value $h = 6.625 \times 10^{-27}$ erg-seconds.

Hyperon: An elementary particle with a mass greater than a neutron. All the known hyperons to date (1962) are strange particles. (*See* Strange particle.)

Indeterminacy: In quantum mechanics, the momentum of a particle in any particular state is always undetermined to a degree that depends on the spatial uncertainty of the particle. This principle was first enunciated by Heisenberg, who showed that the product of the two uncertainties must always be of the order of, or greater than, $h/2\pi$ (*see* Spin). A similar equation also holds for the product of the uncertainty of the energy of the particle and the uncertainty in the time at which the particle possesses that energy.

Ion: In a gas, a charged particle is often referred to as an ion (from the Greek word meaning wanderer) because it can move under the influence of an electric field. A negative ion may be an electron that has been freed from an atom or molecule in the gas; it may also be an electron that has become attached to a neutral atom or molecule. A positive ion is an atom or molecule that has lost one or more electrons.

Isotopic spin: A quantity whose properties in an *isotopic-spin space* are analogous to the properties of ordinary spin in ordinary three-dimensional physical space (*see* Spin *and* Nucleon). In a multiplet of a particular type of particle, the number of charge states of the particle equals $2I + 1$ where I is its isotopic-spin value. The isotopic spins of the strongly interacting particles are as follows: π meson, $I = 1$; K particle, $I = \frac{1}{2}$; nucleon, $I = \frac{1}{2}$; Λ hyperon, $I = O$; Σ hyperon, $I = 1$; Ξ hyperon, $I = \frac{1}{2}$.

Joule: A unit of energy. One kilowatt-hour, which is the unit of electricity used by power companies, is equal to 3,600,000 joules. A mass of 1 kilogram moving with a velocity of 1 meter per second has a kinetic energy of precisely $\frac{1}{2}$ joule.

K particle: A particle with a mass of approximately 970 electron masses. The K particle is a strange particle (*see* Strange particle).

K_1^0 particle: A neutral K particle that lives only 10^{-10} seconds and decays to two π mesons.

K_2^0 particle: A neutral K particle that lives 6×10^{-8} seconds and decays into 3 particles—either 3 mesons or 1 meson and 2 leptons. Any neutral K particle is generally a mixture of both K_1^0 and K_2^0 particles.

Lambda (Λ^0) particle: A neutral particle with a mass of 2183 electron masses.

Lepton: A weakly interacting particle. This group of particles includes electrons, μ mesons, and neutrinos.

Mass-energy: The term of mass is often used loosely and synonymously with matter. Certainly all matter possesses mass, in the sense that all matter has weight (in a gravitational field) and inertia. We do not know yet what property, if any, endows particles with mass. The mass of certain particles can be converted into energy, even without the intermediary of antiparticles. Inversely, also, energy may be used to create certain particles. There is always an equivalence between energy E and mass m given by Einstein's equation: 1.96 times E equals m, where E is the number of Mev and m is the number of electron masses.

Meson: An intermediate mass particle, heavier than an electron and lighter than a proton. Pi mesons and K particles are examples.

Million electron volts (Mev): (*See* Electron volts.)

Mu (μ) meson: A particle rather similar to an electron but much heavier. It has a mass of 207 electron masses.

Negative electricity: The sign of the electric charge may be either positive or negative (terms introduced by Benjamin Franklin). When glass is rubbed with silk, the charge retained on the glass is positive and on the silk is negative.

Neutrino: A zero-mass zero-charge particle that nevertheless has spin and can also carry off energy and momentum. (*See* Energy *and* Recoil momentum.)

Neutron: An electrically neutral elementary particle that, together with the proton, is a basic constituent of nuclei; mass equals 1.675×10^{-24} gram.

Nucleon: A generic term for both proton and neutron. A nucleon has an isotopic-spin value of ½, so that, according to the ideas of multiplets, there are two particles in the nucleon multiplet.

Parity: Positive parity of a particle exists when the sign of the wave function describing the particle does not change upon reversal of the signs of the space coordinates, upon whose specification the wave function depends. In the case of negative parity, the sign does change. This is probably the simplest one-sentence definition of parity that can be given. It does not adequately cover all systems, however. The meaning of intrinsic parity of a particle, for instance, is more fully discussed in Chapter Two where the case of the π-meson parity is considered.

Phasing: Timing of a particle or a pulse with reference to either an oscillation or a circulation.

Pi (π) meson: A Yukawa type of particle associated with nuclear forces; its mass is approximately 270 electron masses.

Positron: A positively charged electron (*see also* Electron charge).

Potential difference: An electric-potential difference exists between two points—either in space or in some material, such as a conductor—when work has to be done to move a positively charged particle from the point of lower potential to the point of higher potential. Similar (but, of course, non-electric) potential differences exist in gravitational- and nuclear-force fields. (*See also* Volt.)

Proton: The nucleus of the simplest atom of hydrogen. The proton, as the name signifies, is the first nuclear particle; its mass is equal to 1.672×10^{-24} gram, or 1836 electron masses; the charge of a proton equals $+1.6 \times 10^{-19}$ coulomb.

Radioactive nucleus: One that is inherently unstable and which will spontaneously decay with a lifetime characteristic of all the nuclei of the same structure as itself.

Radiofrequency: An oscillation of high frequency, for example, lying between 100,000 cycles per second (100 kilocycles/sec) and 1,000,000,000 cycles per second (1000 megacycles/sec).

Recoil momentum: Momentum is defined as the product of the mass of the particle and the velocity of the particle. According to Newton's law, whenever the momentum of a body or particle has changed, a force must have acted on the particle. Momentum is taken up in the recoil of one particle on another. In any recoil of particles against one another, the recoil momentum in one direction is equal and opposite to the amount of recoil in the reverse direction; that is, momentum is conserved.

Sigma (Σ) hyperon: A particle with a mass approximately 2332 electron masses.

Spin: Many fundamental particles possess inherent spin. The electron, neutrino, mu meson, neutron, proton, and hyperons all possess spin. Physically, spin is synonymous with angular momentum. A well-known quantity of angular momentum is $\hbar$, that is Planck's constant h divided by 2π, π being in this case the well-known constant 3.14. The inherent spin of an electron, neutrino, proton, etc., is $(\frac{1}{2})\hbar$ or $h/4\pi$, which is the quantum of spin used in this book. The spin value S, in units of $\hbar$, is termed the spin-quantum number of a particular particle, or simply the spin of a particle. The value of S for the electron, neutrino, or proton is, therefore, $\frac{1}{2}$. One of the fundamental properties of quantum-mechanical spin is that the number of allowed spin-axis orientations relative to any given direction equals precisely $2S + 1$.

Stellar synthesis of elements: Much of the detailed mechanism of how stars synthesize elements was worked out in the period from 1940 to 1960. The youngest stars ($\sim 10^6$ years) as well as the coolest ($\sim 10^7$ degrees absolute) are those forming helium (He^4) from hydrogen (H^1) according to the following so-called proton-proton chain:

$$H^1 + H^1 \rightarrow H^2 + e^+ + \nu$$
$$H^2 + H^1 \rightarrow He^3 + \gamma$$
$$He^3 + He^3 \rightarrow He^4 + H^1 + H^1$$

The next stage of stellar evolution occurs in the helium-burning stars, of which our own sun is an example. In this type of star, which is largely identified with the large body of stars known as the main sequence, helium is converted into higher atoms such as C^{12}, O^{16}, Ne^{20}, etc., according to fusion reactions such as:

$$He^4 + He^4 \rightarrow Be^8$$
$$Be^8 + He^4 \rightarrow C^{12*} \rightarrow C^{12} + \gamma$$

The temperatures of these stars are of the order of a hundred million (10^8) degrees absolute, and the life of the average main sequence of the star is of the order of several hundred million (10^8) years.

Strange particle: One which is produced strongly but which decays slowly. Strange particles are characterized by strangeness quantum numbers that differ from zero. A strange particle will be produced strongly when it is associated with another strange particle so that the total strangeness value does not change. The only strange particles known to date are K particles and hyperons and possible intercombinations of them with non-strange particles.

Tau (τ) particle: A K particle that decays into 3 π mesons.

Theta (θ) particle: A K particle that decays into 2 π mesons. Initially, this term was applied to the neutral V_1^0 particle, which decays in this manner. Later, however, charged particles were also found to decay in this way.

Track: Detectability of a particle is usually only possible because of its charge. The medium is generally ionized along the *track* of the particle; that is, electrons are set free from the atoms of the medium by the energetic charged particle passing close by the atoms of the medium. In the case of either a neutral particle or radiation, detectability is generally only possible if the neutral particle or radiation produces a secondary charged particle, which then causes ionization. Only the starting and stopping or interacting points of neutral particles are therefore generally visible.

V particle: One that has the appearance of a "vee" in a detecting chamber. The most-common types of vees are: V_1^0, which decays into 2 charged π mesons, and V_2^0, which decays into a proton and a π-meson. When either the V_1^0 or the V_2^0 decays while moving at high velocities, the 2 product particles are thrown forward into a vee-like appearance.

Virtual meson: The term *virtual* is applied to any particle that is nascently present. Its real existence can be obtained only by supplying the energy for creating the mass of the particle. Virtual particles are consistent with Heisenberg's principle of indeterminacy in quantum mechanics.

Volt: A unit of electrical potential difference (*see* Potential difference). A battery of cells develops an electric-potential difference across its terminals by means of chemical-potential energy. The potential difference of an ordinary flashlight cell is approximately 1.5 volts.

Wavelength: The distance, for example, between two successive crests of a wave. Many illustrations of waves are available, such as: mechanical waves on the surface of water, along strings, and in air; electromagnetic waves as in light and x rays; and so-called *matter* waves of nuclear and atomic particles. Matter waves were predicted by de Broglie in 1923, and the matter waves of electrons were discovered by Davisson and Germer and by G. P. Thomson in 1925. These developments culminated in the theory of wave mechanics.

Wave function: In quantum mechanics, also known as wave mechanics, the motion of a particle (especially an elementary particle) may be described by a wave equation, usually the Schrödinger wave equation. This equation connects the wave function with the variables of space and time. The probability of finding the particle at a certain instant is proportional to the magnitude of the wave function squared. Modern theoretical physics is very much concerned with first setting up a wave equation for a particular problem and then with finding a solution of the equation.

Wilson cloud chamber: A visual detector of ionizing radiations and particles. A chamber containing gas and saturated water vapor is suddenly expanded. The cooling thereby produced causes condensation of droplets that preferentially form on ions in the gas. The track of a charged particle moving through the gas and producing ions will, therefore, be rendered visible by the droplets formed along the track.

X ray: An electromagnetic radiation similar to visible light, but of a much shorter wavelength. Following a suggestion by Einstein in 1905, radiation is now accepted as being transmitted in packets, or photons. The photons of x rays are very energetic compared with those of visible-light radiation, but usually are taken to be less energetic than photons of gamma rays. High-energy photons are measured in Mev. Visible-light photons are only a few ev.

Xi (Ξ) hyperon: A particle with a mass of approximately 2580 electron masses.

INDEX